MEGAWORDS 1

2nd Edition

Decoding, Spelling, and Understanding
Multisyllabic Words

Kristin Johnson • Polly Bayrd

1 SYLLABLE TYPES AND SYLLABICATION RULES

*background
bedspread
breakfast
somewhere
everywhere
it itself
strawberry
understood
oatmeal
~~tough~~
tonight*

Cara

School Specialty, Inc.
Cambridge and Toronto

Editorial Project Manager: Sethany Rancier Alongi
Editor: Marcy Gilbert

Printed in Mayfield, PA, in December 2009
ISBN 978-0-8388-0900-6

1 2 3 4 5 6 PAH 13 12 11 10 09

Contents

To the Student

Megawords 1: Decoding, Spelling, and Understanding Multisyllabic Words is the first in a series of books designed to help you read and spell words that contain two or more syllables. The lists are organized according to spelling patterns and word structure. Worksheets following each list explain and help you practice the rules or patterns found in that particular group of words. Some exercises focus on reading the words; others focus on spelling or vocabulary.

Megawords is designed to meet your individual learning needs. You and your teacher can decide which lists you need to study (and which you already know) by interpreting your results on the Check Test. You may need to focus on reading and spelling. Or you may need to use **Megawords** only to improve spelling skills. You and your teacher can record your progress on the Accuracy Checklist at the back of your book.

We feel that it is important for you to be able to 1) sound out the words and 2) learn to read them proficiently and fluently. You and your teacher will set a reading rate goal. When you can read the words easily and automatically, you will be less likely to forget the words and you can concentrate on reading for meaning instead of sounding out words. You can keep track of your reading rate on the Word Proficiency Graph at the back of your book. We also feel it is important for you to practice reading the words in connected text. At the end of each lesson is a reading passage that incorporates both list words and review words. In addition to building your comprehension, you can do repeated readings of this passage and chart your fluency rate on the Fluency Graph.

Megawords 1 focuses on six types of syllables and five rules for syllabication. The **Megawords** series assumes that you can already read and spell most one-syllable words, blend isolated sounds to form a syllable, and identify long and short vowels, but we have included one-syllable warm-up pages to better prepare you for working with the multisyllabic words on each list.

We hope that you will be interested in checking out your skills in reading and spelling multisyllabic words—in seeing what you know and what you need to learn. In addition, we hope that you will enjoy tackling new word groups and mastering them. We think that multisyllabic words, when presented clearly and in patterned groups, can be challenging and fun. We sincerely hope that you enjoy and experience success with **Megawords**.

—Polly Bayrd and Kristin Johnson

afternoon	classroom	headache	railroad
airplane	coconut	herself	raincoat
airport	cowhand	himself	sailboat
anyone	daytime	homesick	sidewalk
anything	deckhand	horseback	snowball
anyway	driveway	itself	snowflake
anywhere	drugstore	lookout	snowshoe
background	everyone	maybe	somebody
backpack	everything	moonlight	someone
barefoot	everywhere	myself	something
baseball	fishhook	necktie	sometimes
battleship	football	newspaper	somewhere
become	footstep	notebook	strawberry
bedroom	forget	oatmeal	streetcar
bedspread	forgive	outfit	sunshine
belong	forgot	outlaw	today
below	friendship	outside	tonight
beside	gentleman	pancake	understand
birthday	grandfather	peanut	understood
bluebird	grandmother	pineapple	washtub
breakfast	grapefruit	playground	wastebasket
butterfly	graveyard	playmate	without
cardboard	handball	pocketbook	workshop
carload	haystack	popcorn	yourself

Compound Words

Some long words are **compound words**. A compound word is a word made up of two smaller related words.

Examples: *class/room:* a room where a class meets

snow/shoe: a shoe worn in the snow

It is easier to read compound words if you can find the smaller words inside them.

(1) These small words are often parts of compound words. Practice reading them aloud.

be	out	look	some
where	my	one	her
him	wash	for	work
play	get	walk	may

(2) These words can also be parts of compound words. Practice reading them aloud.

day	coat	sail	law
snow	room	straw	rail
stood	rain	load	look
book	ground	noon	out

(3) Now your teacher will dictate some of these words. Say each word as you write it.

1. _____   7. _____

2. _____   8. _____

3. _____   9. _____

4. _____   10. _____

5. _____   11. _____

6. _____   12. _____

① Say each small word to read the compound word. Circle the small words as shown.

news	paper	(news)(paper)	snow	shoe	snowshoe
some	body	somebody	out	law	outlaw
any	one	anyone	sun	shine	sunshine
class	room	classroom	card	board	cardboard
grave	yard	graveyard	drive	way	driveway
air	plane	airplane	rain	coat	raincoat
butter	fly	butterfly	drug	store	drugstore

② Match two small words to make a compound word.

may	pack	_maybe_	bed	self	_____
back	body	_____	cow	road	_____
some	ground	_____	him	day	_____
play	be	_____	rail	long	_____
neck	book	_____	birth	hand	_____
note	tie	_____	be	room	_____

③ Now circle these twenty-five compound words in the word search below. The words can be found across or down.

```
N C L A S S R O O M R A I N C O A T B E L O N G
O A N Y O N E S E A A N T C E N E W S P A P E R
T B D R I V E W A Y I P L A Y G R O U N D M C A
E S N O W S H O E B L E N C O B A C K P A C K V
B B I R T H D A Y E R R R B U T T E R F L Y T E
O U T L A W E C T T O H C A R D B O A R D E I Y
O S U N S H I N E A A X S H O A I R P L A N E A
K H I M S E L F B E D R O O M W N A C G P T K R
D R U G S T O R E S O M E B O D Y C O W H A N D
```

Any, some, and *every* are often found at the beginning of compound words.

1 **Write the small word on the lines. Then write the compound word.**

any

_____where   _____

_____way   _____

_____one   _____

_____thing   _____

_____body   _____

some

_____where   _____

_____body   _____

_____one   _____

_____thing   _____

every

_____where   _____

_____body   _____

_____one   _____

_____thing   _____

2 **QUICK CHECK** **Have another student test you on spelling these words.**

My score: _____ / _____ words correct

Self, where, be, and *out* are often found in compound words.

1 Write the small word on the lines. Then write the compound word.

self

your_____   _____

it_____   _____

my_____   _____

her_____   _____

where

any_____   _____

every_____   _____

some_____   _____

no_____   _____

be

_____side   _____

_____come   _____

may_____   _____

_____long   _____

out

look_____   _____

_____law   _____

with_____   _____

_____side   _____

2 **QUICK CHECK** Have another student test you on spelling these words.

My score: _____ / _____ words correct

1 Your teacher will dictate ten compound words. Choose one word from each column, and then write the compound word.

side	plane	_____
air	mother	_____
look	load	_____
pop	corn	_____
any	walk	_____
car	out	_____
grand	one	_____
hand	board	_____
card	store	_____
drug	ball	_____

2 Your teacher will dictate ten compound words. Spell the missing word, and say the whole compound word as you write it.

1. _____road   _____
2. _____ball   _____
3. _____be   _____
4. _____where   _____
5. _____hook   _____
6. snow_____   _____
7. back_____   _____
8. hay_____   _____
9. with_____   _____
10. bed_____   _____

(1) Draw a line between the small words to divide the compound words. Write the small words on the blank lines. Say them aloud as you spell.

horse|back	_horse_	_back_
pancake	_____	_____
sailboat	_____	_____
Sunday	_____	_____
outside	_____	_____
moonlight	_____	_____
driveway	_____	_____
snowball	_____	_____
peanut	_____	_____
playground	_____	_____
tonight	_____	_____
forgive	_____	_____
lookout	_____	_____
bluebird	_____	_____
snowflake	_____	_____

Proofreading Practice

Two of the List 1 words are misspelled in each of the sentences. Cross out each misspelled word, and write the correct spelling above it.

1. A burthday is no fun withowt cake and ice cream.

2. Will someone please order oatmeel for the football player's breckfast?

3. Tonite I heard footsteps on the driveway outsid my grandmother's bedroom.

Practice Page 1G

① Your teacher will dictate ten compound words. Write the small words on the first two lines, and write the compound word on the third. Say the words as you write them.

1. _____ _____ _____
2. _____ _____ _____
3. _____ _____ _____
4. _____ _____ _____
5. _____ _____ _____
6. _____ _____ _____
7. _____ _____ _____
8. _____ _____ _____
9. _____ _____ _____
10. _____ _____ _____

② Complete the puzzle with the compound words from above.

Across
2. morning meal
4. opposite of inside
5. a thing that is not definite
6. the room where you sleep
7. the mark your feet leave
8. this evening
9. perhaps

Down
1. opposite of *remembered*
2. to be a part of
3. anybody

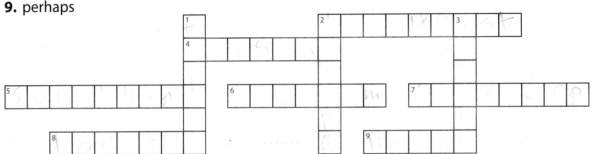

⑤ **Review**

A _____ word is a longer word made up of two smaller related words (*class/room, snow/shoe*).

Some compound words can be taken apart to make a definition of the whole word.
Example: A *snowflake* is a *flake* of *snow*.

1 **Use the small words inside the compound word to complete the sentences.**

1. A bedspread can be _____ spread _____ on a _____ bed _____ .

2. A sidewalk is a place to _____ on the _____ of the road.

3. A raincoat is a _____ to use in the _____ .

4. A necktie is something you can _____ around your _____ .

5. A notebook is a _____ to use for writing a _____ .

6. A washtub is a _____ for the _____ .

2 **Fill in the blanks with words from the box.**

forgot	outlaw	snowshoes	backpack	belong
maybe	pineapples	coconuts	grapefruit	forgive
himself	outside	birthday		

1. _____ , _____ , and _____ are three fruits that grow in warm places.

2. The _____ gave _____ up to the police.

3. Do not take things that don't _____ to you.

4. _____ we can go _____ when it stops raining.

5. Joanne took her _____ and _____ when she went camping in the snow.

6. I could not _____ myself if I _____ your _____ .

(1) **Read the sentences and circle all the List 1 words.**

1. Luisa and her grandmother bought her grandfather a necktie for his birthday.

2. The deckhand on the battleship saw a sailboat in the moonlight.

3. The cowhand rode horseback past the graveyard.

4. Kim and her playmate like to skate on the sidewalk near the playground.

5. The gentleman ate oatmeal for breakfast.

6. Everyone at the football game ate popcorn.

7. Be on the lookout for a carload of boys and girls carrying snowshoes.

8. The bedspread hung outside to dry in the sunshine.

9. Sometimes Derek forgets to do his chores in the afternoon.

10. The airport is six miles from the railroad track.

11. Someone will understand what Tom wrote in his notebook.

(2) **Your teacher will dictate three of the sentences above. Write them on a blank piece of paper.**

(3) **Write a short story or descriptive paragraph using ten words from List 1. Be creative!**

✓ **Reading and Spelling Skill Check**

Demonstrate your accuracy in reading and spelling List 1 words. Your teacher will select ten words to read and ten words to spell. Record your scores on the Accuracy Checklist. Work toward 90–100 percent accuracy.

Word Proficiency

Now build up your reading proficiency with List 1 words. Decide on your rate goal with your teacher. Record your progress on the Word Proficiency Graph.

My goal for reading List 1 is _____ words per minute with two or fewer errors.

1 Practice the words, read the passage, and then answer the questions.

List 1 Words			Passage Words	
forget	pancakes	yourself	morning	research
breakfast	strawberry	without	important	students
oatmeal	pineapple	classroom	fuel	
grapefruit	coconut		cranky	

Don't Forget Breakfast!

Of all the meals, breakfast gets skipped the most. It is easy to forget about it in the morning rush. If you miss breakfast, you are missing the most important meal of the day.

What makes breakfast so important? When you wake up in the morning, you need fuel for the day. Breakfast gives you that fuel. Without it, you may become sleepy or cranky.

The best breakfast foods are the ones that are good for you. Here are a few choices:

• Oatmeal with grapefruit slices.

• Whole grain pancakes with a fresh strawberry or two.

• Pineapple slices with coconut.

Eating one of these meals can make your day in the classroom go much better. Research shows that students who eat a good breakfast do well on tests. Plus, they don't get sick as much as students who don't eat breakfast.

So, the next time you head out of the house, ask yourself, "Did I forget the most important meal of the day?"

1. What word from the text means "a type of breakfast cereal"? _____

2. How might someone feel after skipping breakfast? _____

3. Why do you think a student who skips breakfast would be sick more than a student

who never does? Explain. _____

2 **FLUENCY** Record your progress on the Fluency Graph.

My goal for reading the passage is _____ words per minute with two or fewer errors.

/ă/		/ĕ/	/ĭ/	/ŏ/	/ŭ/
absent	frantic	dental	children	blossom	button
actress	gallon	dentist	chipmunk	bonnet	custom
address	gallop	enchant	infant	bottom	hundred
annex	happen	hectic	infect	coffin	husband
atlas	magnet	lesson	insect	collect	muffin
attic	mammal	mental	insult	common	musket
bandit	mantis	pretzel	kidnap	congress	nutmeg
basket	mascot	seldom	kitten	connect	public
blanket	napkin	selfish	mitten	conquest	publish
cactus	rabbit	splendid	Phillip	consent	pumpkin
campus	random	tendon	picnic	contact	puppet
candid	sandal	tennis	pilgrim	contest	subject
canyon	sandwich	velvet	quintet	convict	subtract
catnip	tablet		ribbon	cotton	sudden
channel	talcum		signal	fossil	trumpet
Dallas	traffic		tinsel	goblet	tunnel
flannel			wisdom	goblin	until
				gossip	
				object	
				optic	
				ostrich	
				problem	
				progress	
				tonsil	

Three-Syllable Words:

Atlantic　　establish　　Wisconsin　　badminton　　fantastic

What Is a Syllable?

A **syllable** is a group of letters that has one vowel sound. A syllable can be a word or part of a word.

Words:
stay   miss   stripe   I

Parts of words:
op   lect   pre

The Closed Syllable (VC)

One type of syllable is called a **closed syllable** (VC).

There are three things to remember about the closed syllable:

1. It has only one vowel (V).
2. The vowel has a short sound.
3. It ends in a consonant (C).

Closed-syllable words: at   big   must

(1) Read the closed-syllable words. Then add two more closed-syllable words under each heading.

/ă/	/ĕ/	/ĭ/	/ŏ/	/ŭ/
add	end	it	on	up
lag	get	ill	stop	mud
flap	spent	sift	clock	trust
band	step	skip	pod	club
_____	_____	_____	_____	_____
_____	_____	_____	_____	_____

(2) Now your teacher will dictate some closed-syllable words. Say each word as you write it.

1. _____
2. _____
3. _____
4. _____
5. _____
6. _____

Closed Syllables: Parts of Words

These closed syllables have only one vowel, and they end in a consonant.
The vowel sound is short.

Examples: fran ab cus tist

(1) **Circle the closed syllables.**

gos	pret	trum	cade	lish
fle	sud	op	flan	prob
tal	cu	hus	sel	tain
vict	tist	caul	ject	ap
blos	lete	chil	tact	ple

(2) **Now write the closed syllables under the correct headings. Make sure to give the vowel its short sound when you say each syllable.**

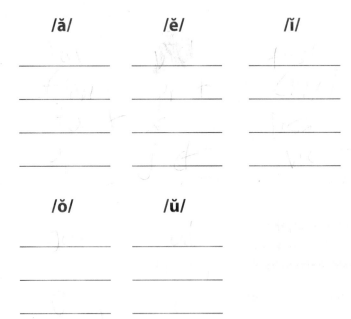

/ă/	/ĕ/	/ĭ/
_____	_____	_____
_____	_____	_____
_____	_____	_____
_____	_____	_____

/ŏ/	/ŭ/
_____	_____
_____	_____
_____	_____

Review

Underline the correct word in each parentheses.

- A closed syllable has *(one, two)* vowel(s).
- The vowel has a *(long, short)* sound.
- The syllable ends in a *(vowel, consonant)*.

1 Read the syllables. Write *closed* if the syllable is closed, and mark the vowel short. 100%
If the syllable is not closed, explain why.

pŭs	closed	li	
loo	no consonant at end, 2 vowels	com	
cle		lope	
vel		trich	
mu		nee	
os		plode	
tume		nex	
min		gra	
crea		sil	
prob		ple	

2 **EXCEPTION** When *qu* is found in a word, the *u* does not have a vowel sound and will always be followed by a vowel. Therefore, the following syllables are closed. Make sure to give the vowel its short sound when you say each syllable.

quin   quest   quiv   quit   ques   quill

closed

Syllables often end in the consonant blend *ct*. Many students have trouble spelling this blend because it is hard to hear.

① Add *ct* to the end of each syllable below. Then write the whole syllable, and say it aloud as you spell it. Make sure each vowel letter has a short sound.

fe_____   _____   vi_____   _____

se_____   _____   ta_____   _____

je_____   _____   le_____   _____

② Your teacher will dictate twelve closed syllables. Repeat each syllable as you spell it.

1. _____   7. _____

2. _____   8. _____

3. _____   9. _____

4. _____   10. _____

5. _____   11. _____

6. _____   12. _____

③ Circle the *ct* syllable in these words.

in(fect)	dejected	evict	detractor
reject	insect	tactical	elect
select	injected	subtract	convict
subject	subtracting	convicted	insecticide

⑤ *Review*

If you hear a short-vowel sound in a syllable:

What kind of syllable is it? _____

How many vowels does it have? _____

Is the last letter a vowel or a consonant? _____

Closed Syllable Words

Many words are formed by putting two closed syllables together. The vowel sounds in each syllable of these words will be short.

1 Mark the vowels short (˘). Say the syllables to read the whole word. Then draw a line between the syllables as shown.

cŏn	tăct	con|tact	ăd	dress	address
nut	meg	nutmeg	con	test	contest
mas	cot	mascot	in	sect	insect
pub	lish	publish	sel	fish	selfish
con	vict	convict	quin	tet	quintet
hec	tic	hectic	cac	tus	cactus
at	tic	attic	tal	cum	talcum
un	til	until			

2 Read the definitions. Choose the correct word from above, and write it on the line.

kind of desert plant _____

chance for someone to win _____

thinking only of oneself _____

bug _____

type of powder _____

group of five _____

spice _____

person in prison _____

space just below the roof _____

where someone lives _____

Schwa Sound

When two closed syllables make a two-syllable word, the vowel in the second syllable often does NOT make its expected short sound. Instead, it will have either a short *i* or the **schwa** sound, which sounds like short *u* (/ŭ/).

The schwa sound is the same for all vowels. It is marked with the symbol /ə/. It is found only in an unaccented syllable, which is the second syllable of List 2 words.

① **Mark the first vowel short (˘) and circle the syllable with the schwa sound. Say the syllables to read the whole word. Then draw a line between the syllables as shown.**

băn	(dit)	ban|dit	kit	ten	kitten
gob	lin	goblin	hus	band	husband
pret	zel	pretzel	hap	pen	happen
tin	sel	tinsel	san	dal	sandal
vel	vet	velvet	bas	ket	basket
sub	ject	subject	sel	dom	seldom
ton	sil	tonsil	gal	lon	gallon

② **Read the definitions. Choose the correct word from above, and write it on the line.**

male spouse _____

not often _____

ugly, sneaky elf _____

robber _____

thin strips of shiny metal foil _____

type of summer shoe _____

soft, thick cloth _____

snack food _____

topic _____

1 Read the first syllable. Choose the correct second syllable to make a real word. Say each word as you write it.

	vict		ress		wich
mag	tom	prog	nel	hun	dred
	net		dom		pen

magnet

_____   _____   _____

	sip		sil		tic
sel	meg	ton	let	fran	vet
	fish		nap		nel

_____   _____   _____

2 Match the syllables to make real words. Say each word as you write it.

den   zel   _____   trum   dom   _____

hus   tist   _____   sel   nel   _____

pret   band   _____   tun   pet   _____

con   tus   _____   prob   nel   _____

cac   den   _____   flan   tress   _____

sud   test   _____   ac   lem   _____

3 Unscramble the syllables to make a real word.

tas   tic   fan   _____

lish   es   tab   _____

bad   ton   min   _____

lan   At   tic   _____

sin   con   Wis   _____

Practice Page   2H

1 Your teacher will dictate twenty words. Spell the missing syllable. Then say the whole word as you write it.

1. _____ cum   _____

2. _____ ket   _____

3. _____ bon   _____

4. _____ did   X _____

5. _____ tract   _____

6. _____ las   _____

7. _____ pet   _____

8. _____ trich   _____

9. _____ dom   _____

10. _____ grim   X _____

11. _____ tist   _____

12. _____ lem   _____

13. kid _____   _____

14. sel _____   _____

15. in _____   _____

16. con _____   _____

17. cac _____   _____

18. nut _____   _____

19. con _____   _____

20. es tab _____   _____

---

⑤ Review

If a syllable is closed, the vowel sound is _____. A closed syllable has

only _____ vowel and ends in a _____.

Review

The second syllable of a two-syllable word often has the short-*i* sound or the schwa sound (/ə/). These sounds can be difficult to spell because all of the vowels can make the sound, and you have to remember which vowel to use.

The pattern *et* is a common way to spell /ət/ or /ĭt/ at the end of words.

1 **Fill in the missing letters *et*, and write the whole word.**

gob l_____   _____goblet_____

bas k_____   _____

pup p_____   _____

blan k_____   _____

vel v_____   _____

mag n_____   _____

trum p_____   _____

tab l_____   _____

2 **Read the clues. Choose the correct word from Activity 1, and write it on the line.**

a horn   _____

a soft fabric   _____

a toy   _____

a bed cover   _____

a fancy glass with a stem   _____

a pad of paper   _____

something that attracts metal   _____

a straw container   _____

5/7/10

Practice Page | 2J |

ic is a common spelling for /ĭk/ at the end of two- and three-syllable words.

(1) Fill in the missing syllable *tic*, and write each word next to the correct definition.

fran _tic_	**1.** having to do with the eye	_optic_
At lan _tic_	**2.** super	_fantastic_
op _tic_	**3.** wild with pain or fear	_frantic_
hec _tic_	**4.** large ocean	_Atlantic_
at _tic_	**5.** confusing; filled with excitement	_hectic_
fan tas _tic_	**6.** space just below the roof	_attic_

The pattern *om* is a common way to spell /əm/ at the end of words.

(2) Find the missing *om*, and write each word next to the correct definition.

ran d _om_	**1.** flower	_blossom_
cus t _om_	**2.** by chance	_random_
sel d _om_	**3.** habit	_custom_
blos s _om_	**4.** lowest part	_bottom_
bot t _om_	**5.** not often	_seldom_

(3) EXCEPTION /əm/ at the end of *problem* is spelled *em*. Practice writing the word.

problem   _problem_   _problem_

⑤ *Review*

How do you spell these common endings?

/ət/ = _et_ as in bask _et_

/ĭk/ = _ic_ as in att _ic_

/əm/ = _em_ as in bott _om_

VC/CV Syllabication Rule

When two consonants (C) stand between two vowels (V), you divide the word between the consonants.

Example: at | la s
v c | c v

The first vowel sound is usually short because the syllable is closed. In List 2 words, the second syllable is also closed and the second vowel sound will either be short /ˇ/ or schwa /ə/.

(1) **Directions:**

- Circle the vowel letters.

- Draw a line between the consonants.

- Mark the first vowel sound short.

Example: selfish

dis|cuss	ton|sil	mag|net
fran|tic	ten|don	man|tis
pret|zel	op|tic	mas|cot
un|til	den|tal	ran|dom
tal|cum	con|tact	quin|tet
tin|sel	prog|ress	an|nex

(2) Now read the words above to your teacher or another student.

ⓢ *Review*

VC/CV Syllabication Rule: If two consonants stand between two vowels, you divide the word between the _____.

If three consonants stand between two vowels, you divide the word between the consonants so that consonant blends *(tr, dr, nd, mp, gr)* and digraphs *(ch, th, sh, wh)* stay together.

① Circle the blends and digraphs, and draw a line to divide the words into syllables. Then write the syllables on the lines.

	First Syllable	Second Syllable
con(gr)ess	con	gress
hun(dr)ed	hun	dred
pum(pk)in	pump	pkin
os(tr)ich	os	trich
pil(gr)im	pil	grim
ac(tr)ess	ac	tress
ad(dr)ess	ad	dress
sand(w)ich	sand	dwich

② Use the VC/CV Rule to divide these three-syllable words.

	First Syllable	Second Syllable	Third Syllable
establish	es	tab	lish
badminton	bad	min	ton
fantastic	fan	tas	tic
Wisconsin	Wis	con	sin
Atlantic	At	lan	tic

Spelling Variations

When you hear /ən/ at the end of two-syllable words, you will use one of these spellings:

on as in *ribbon*　　　**en** as in *kitten*　　　**in** as in *napkin*

① Circle the last two letters in each word. Then write the words under the correct heading.

napkin	*happen	*cotton	common	*ribbon	Wisconsin
*sudden	*children	*gallon	mitten	*kitten	pumpkin
muffin	*lesson	coffin	tendon	*button	badminton

on Words	*en* Words	*in* Words
gallon	sudden	napkin
lesson	happen	muffin
cotton	kitten	coffin
common	mitten	pumpkin
tendon	children	Wisconsin
ribbon		
button		
badminton		

② Fill in the blanks with the starred words from Activity 1.

One sunny day, Dad was driving the _____children_____ to their tennis _____lesson_____ when all of a _____sudden_____ the car ran out of gas. They all walked to get a _____gallon_____ of gas. On the way, Eve lost her hair _____ribbon_____, a _____button_____ fell off Vance's _____cotton_____ shirt, and Rick found a lost _____kitten_____. What would _____happen_____ next?

Double Middle Consonant Spelling Rule

In a two-syllable word, when you hear one consonant after the first short vowel sound, double it.

Examples: ga**ll**op ri**bb**on

(1) **Fill in the missing letters. Then say the syllables aloud as you write the whole words.**

child's toy	pu _p p_ et	puppet
used to tie something	ri _b b_ on	ribbon
game two people play	te _n n_ is	tennis
baby cat	ki _t t_ en	kitten
lowest part	bo _t t_ om	bottom
humans, cats, dogs, horses	ma _m m_ als	mammals
faster than a trot	ga _l l_ op	gallop
talk about other people	go _s s_ ip	gossip
four quarts	ga _l l_ on	gallon
used to bury people	co _f f_ in	coffin
underground passage	tu _n n_ el	tunnel
something added on	a _n n_ ex	annex
type of cloth	co _t t_ on	cotton
type of cloth	fla _n n_ el	flannel
usual	co _m m_ on	common
small, round cake or bread	mu _f f_ in	muffin
something to be learned	le _s s_ on	lesson
to fasten	bu _t t_ on	button
just below the roof	a _t t_ ic	attic

(2) **QUICK CHECK** Now have another student test you on spelling some of the words above.

My score: _____ / _____ words correct

1 Directions:

• Your teacher will dictate a two- or three-syllable word.

• Repeat the word.

• Isolate and pronounce the syllables, saying the sounds as you spell.

• Combine the syllables and write the whole word, saying the sounds as you spell.

1. | den | tist | _dentist_
2. | bas | ket | _basket_
3. | sud | den | _sudden_
4. | sig | nal | _signal_
5. | prob | lem | _problem_
6. | hap | pen | _happen_
7. | sub | ject | _subject_
8. | sel | fish | _selfish_
9. | es | tab | lish | _establish_
10. | fan | tas | tic | _fantastic_

2 Fill in the blanks with words from above.

1. All of a _____sudden_____, Al dropped the picnic _____basket_____.

2. The new _____dentist_____ plans to _____establish_____ herself in this office.

3. Miguel was so _____selfish_____ that he had a _____problem_____ making friends.

Practice Page 2P

1 Fill in the blanks with words from the box.

absent	selfish	napkins	tennis	sandwich
until	contest	rabbit	hundred	subject
address	dentist	husband	problem	insect

1. Randal's best __subject__ is math. She got one __hundred__ percent on the test.

2. I have to go to the __dentist__ to get a tooth filled.

3. Let's play __tennis__ __until__ 4:00 p.m.

4. Elvin was __absent__ from school on the day we had the spelling __contest__.

5. Please fix me a ham __sandwich__ for lunch.

6. If you give Emma your __address__, she can write you a letter.

7. An __insect__ bit me.

8. Nick is very __selfish__. His __problem__ is that he only cares about himself.

9. A __rabbit__ was eating the flowers in our backyard. My __husband__ set out a trap to catch it.

10. Be sure to put __napkins__ on the table.

2 **QUICK CHECK** Now have another student test you on spelling some of these words.

My score: __14__ / __15__ words correct

① **Replace the underlined words with a word from the box. Write the word on the line.**

mammals	tendon	annexed	candid
goblets	mascot	quintet	mantis
optic	published	random	

1. The bear is the <u>good luck animal</u> for the Chicago football team. _____mascot_____

2. My sister wrote a book that will be <u>printed</u> next year. _____published_____

3. I gave Lee a set of <u>drinking glasses</u> for her wedding. _____goblets_____

4. Humans, horses, dogs, lions, and whales are all <u>animals that feed milk to their young</u>. _____mammals_____

5. Finn was not listening and gave a <u>chance</u> answer to the teacher's question. _____random_____

6. The United States <u>added</u> Alaska and Hawaii as new states in 1959. _____annexed_____

7. Skye hurt a <u>piece of tissue that joins muscle to bone</u> when she was playing football. _____tendon_____

8. Raj was very <u>frank</u> about his reasons for wanting to change jobs. _____candid_____

9. We want this <u>insect</u> in our flower bed because it eats other insects. _____mantis_____

10. The <u>group of five players</u> had a trumpet, a sax, a bass, a keyboard, and a set of drums. _____quintet_____

11. The <u>eye</u> nerve connects the eye to the brain. _____optic_____

Cara 5/24/10

✎ **Proofreading Practice**

Two of the List 2 words are misspelled in each sentence. Rewrite the whole sentence, and spell the words correctly.

1. How did it happen that Nick was abbsent from his first tennus class?

   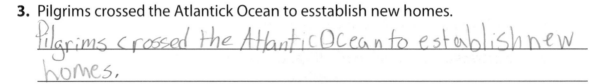
   How did it happen that Nick was absent from his tennis class?

2. Keeping insects away from your sandwitch at a picnic is a common problom.

   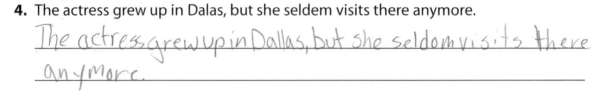
   Keeping insects away from your sandwich at a picnic is a common problem.

3. Pilgrims crossed the Atlantick Ocean to esstablish new homes.

   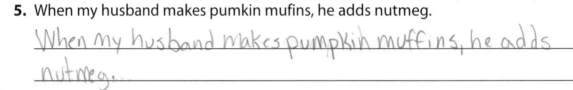
   Pilgrims crossed the Atlantic Ocean to establish new homes.

4. The actress grew up in Dalas, but she seldem visits there anymore.

   The actress grew up in Dallas, but she seldom visits there anymore.

5. When my husband makes pumkin mufins, he adds nutmeg.

   When my husband makes pumpkin muffins, he adds nutmeg.

6. Tim contated the quintet about giving the children a leson.

   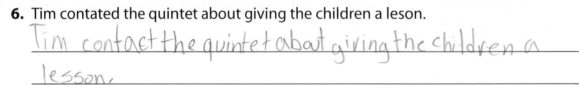
   Tim contact the quintet about giving the children a lesson.

7. Jane found an old bonnet with long ribbens in the atic.

   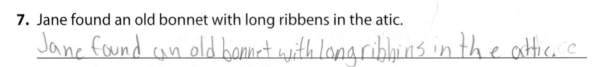
   Jane found an old bonnet with long ribbins in the attice

8. The note on the tablit says that the denist won the contest.

   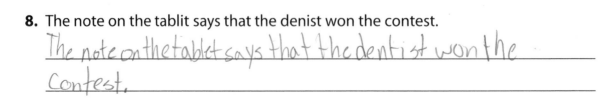
   The note on the tablet says that the dentist won the contest.

① Read the sentences and circle all the List 2 words.

1. Cole took a basket of food and a blanket to the picnic.

2. Max wrote notes on his tablet about his best subject.

3. The tennis team had a chipmunk as its mascot.

4. The children had a splendid time playing with the kitten.

5. Please get me a gallon of milk, a bag of pretzels, and some nutmeg at the store.

6. Donna played her trumpet on the campus common.

7. It is common to have problems with your wisdom teeth.

8. What will happen if Phillip's tonsils get infected?

9. You will get a blue ribbon if you win the contest.

10. The actress ate a pumpkin muffin and a sandwich.

11. Contact me if you and your husband want to join us for a game of badminton.

② Your teacher will dictate three of the sentences above. Write them on a blank piece of paper.

③ Write a short story or descriptive paragraph using ten words from List 2. Be creative!

✓ Reading & Spelling Skill Check

Demonstrate your accuracy in reading and spelling List 2 words. Your teacher will select ten words to read and ten words to spell. Record your scores on the Accuracy Checklist. Work toward 90–100 percent accuracy.

Word Proficiency

Now build up your reading proficiency with List 2 words. Decide on your rate goal with your teacher. Record your progress on the Word Proficiency Graph.

My goal for reading List 2 is _____ words per minute with two or fewer errors.

1 Practice the words, read the passage, and then answer the questions.

List 2 Words			Review Words		Passage Words	
Phillip	traffic	sudden	maybe	everyone	thought	finish
Atlantic	problem	tendon	today	himself	people	toward
hundred	progress	ribbon			ahead	through
signal	galloping	until				

The Road Race

"Maybe today is the day," thought Phillip. It was the start of the Atlantic Road Race, and hundreds of runners waited for the signal.

The starting shot went off. At first, it was like a traffic jam of people, so it was hard to get going. That wasn't a problem for long. Soon the pack thinned out, and Phillip moved ahead.

Phillip kept a good pace, but he was not happy with his progress. Everyone was galloping past him. He ran faster.

In the last stretch of the race, Phillip was in the lead. Then, all of a sudden, he tripped on a pothole in the road and fell. He was in a lot of pain, and he thought he might have pulled a tendon in his leg. But he saw the finish line ahead. He got up and slowly limped toward it.

"Maybe I didn't get to run through the ribbon," Phillip said after the race, "but at least I crossed the line." And Phillip told himself that it would not be long until he was running again.

1. What word from the text means "running very quickly"? _____

2. Why wasn't Phillip happy with his progress? _____

_____

3. Do you think Phillip wanted to quit the race? Explain. _____

_____

2 **FLUENCY** Record your progress on the Fluency Graph.

My goal for reading the passage is _____ words per minute with two or fewer errors.

/ā/	/ē/	/ī/	/ō/	/ū/ and /o͞o/
cascade	athlete	admire	backbone	accuse
compare	compete	advice	backstroke	commune
dictate	complete	advise	compote	compute
escape	concrete	collide	enclose	conclude
estate	extreme	combine	explode	confuse
inflate	stampede	confide	explore	consume
inhale		connive	expose	costume
insane		contrive	ignore	dispute
invade		describe	oppose	excuse
landscape		empire	suppose	immune
membrane		entire	tadpole	include
mistake		hemline	trombone	intrude
octane		ignite		pollute
pancake		incline		
stagnate		inquire		
translate		inside		
welfare		invite		
		pastime		
		reptile		
		retire		
		subscribe		
		sunrise		
		sunshine		
		textile		
		umpire		

Three-Syllable Words:

compensate	confiscate	contemplate	illustrate
indispose	infantile	infiltrate	

The Silent-*e* Syllable (VC*e*)

A **silent-*e* syllable (VC*e*)** has one vowel followed by a consonant and an *e*. The *e* is silent and makes the preceding vowel long (*āce, hīde, dōme*).

(1) These single-syllable words all have a silent *e*. Read the words aloud.

cute	bone	plume	here
late	these	close	tide
line	shape	take	pole
drive	rude	rise	chose

(2) Write the words from Activity 1 under the correct headings.

/ā/	/ē/	/ī/	/ō/	/ū/ or /o͞o/
_____	_____	_____	_____	_____
_____	_____	_____	_____	_____
_____		_____	_____	_____
		_____	_____	

(3) Your teacher will dictate some one-syllable words. Say each word as you write it.

1. _____

2. _____

3. _____

4. _____

5. _____

6. _____

Review

A **closed syllable (VC)** has only one vowel, ends in a consonant, and has a short-vowel sound *(trŏm, ĕm, jĕct).*

① Write the syllables under the correct headings.

pire	pas	rise	con	trive
cuse	tane	vade	pede	flate
trom	stag	wel	in	sume
en	ig	mem	treme	rep

Silent-*e* Syllables   **Closed Syllables**

_____   _____   _____   _____

_____   _____   _____   _____

_____   _____   _____   _____

_____   _____   _____   _____

_____   _____   _____   _____

② Your teacher will dictate ten syllables. Say each syllable as you write it under the correct heading.

Silent-*e* Syllables   **Closed Syllables**

_____   _____

_____   _____

_____   _____

_____   _____

_____   _____

③ Circle the silent-*e* syllables in the words below.

em(pire)   invade   contrive   extreme   consume

Review

VC/CV Syllabication Rule: When two or more consonants stand between two vowels, divide the word between the consonants so that consonant blends and digraphs stay together. The first vowel has a short sound because it is a closed syllable.

(1) **Directions:**

- **Underline the closed syllables.**
- **Circle the silent-*e* syllables.**
- **Say each syllable, and then read the whole word.**
- **Draw a line between the syllables.**

in	(vade)	in|v a d e	dic	tate	d i c t a t e
en	close	e n c l o s e	cas	cade	c a s c a d e
em	pire	e m p i r e	rep	tile	r e p t i l e
oc	tane	o c t a n e	con	crete	c o n c r e t e
col	lide	c o l l i d e	cos	tume	c o s t u m e
ex	treme	e x t r e m e	um	pire	u m p i r e

com	pen	sate	c o m p e n s a t e
il	lus	trate	i l l u s t r a t e
con	tem	plate	c o n t e m p l a t e
in	fan	tile	i n f a n t i l e
in	dis	pose	i n d i s p o s e
con	fis	cate	c o n f i s c a t e

(2) **Now answer these questions about the words above.**

1. The first syllable in each word is a _____ syllable.

2. The last syllable in each word is a _____ syllable.

1 Match the syllables to make real words. Then say each word as you write it.

im	lete	_immune_	trom	vade	_____
es	cape	_____	con	bone	_____
ath	mune	_____	in	crete	_____
in	tume	_____	tad	mune	_____
cos	pede	_____	com	tane	_____
stam	trude	_____	oc	pole	_____
con	take	_____	ig	tile	_____
mis	plode	_____	em	nite	_____
ex	fide	_____	rep	pire	_____

2 Unscramble the syllables to make a real word.

sate	com	pen	_____
con	cate	fis	_____
fan	in	tile	_____
trate	lus	il	_____
in	trate	fil	_____

1 Your teacher will dictate ten words. Spell the missing syllable. Then say the whole word as you write it.

1. _____pire   _____

2. _____crete   _____

3. _____nore   _____

4. _____pole   _____

5. _____plore   _____

6. in_____   _____

7. dic_____   _____

8. in_____   _____

9. oc_____   _____

10. stag_____   _____

---

⑤ Review

1. A _____ syllable has only one vowel, ends in a consonant, and has a short-vowel sound.

2. A _____ syllable has one long vowel followed by one consonant followed by an *e*. The *e* is silent and makes the preceding vowel long.

3. The VC/CV Syllabication Rule says when two or more _____ stand between two _____, you divide between the _____ so that blends and digraphs stay together.

1 Directions:

- Circle the vowels.

- Draw a line between the consonants so that consonant blends and digraphs stay together.

- Mark the vowel sounds long (ˉ) or short (˘).

- Read the words to your teacher or another student.

trans|late   empire   trombone   dictate   explore   athlete

expose   sunshine   invite   cascade   reptile   illustrate

stagnate   stampede   intrude   costume   concrete   infantile

2 In seven of the words in Activity 1, you left a consonant blend or digraph together. Separate these words into syllables, and write them on the lines. Circle the blend or digraph.

_____sun_____   _____(sh)ine_____   _____   _____

_____   _____   _____   _____

_____   _____

_____   _____

3 Circle the eighteen words from Activity 1 in the word search below. The words can be found across or down.

I N T R U D E E X P L O R E P T I L E T E S
M O R E P T I S T A M P E D E I N V I T X U
V D O C O S T U M E E A X R M E V I C O R N
I A M P I R E N O M E M P I R E I M P I R S
T P B T R A N S L A T E O L O A T H L E T E
R T O M B O N H I N C A S C A D E O O X R S
A I N F A N T I L E N E E O D U C T R I A O
N Z E S T A G N A T E I L L U S T R A T E M
S E C O N C R E T E D I C T A T E X M I N E

1 Draw a line to divide between the consonants (VC/CV). Circle the consonant blends or digraphs that stay together. Then say the word as you write each syllable.

e s c a p e   _____ _____

i n q u i r e   _____ _____

c o m p l e t e   _____ _____

d i s p u t e   _____ _____

t r a n s l a t e   _____ _____

a d m i r e   _____ _____

e x t r e m e   _____ _____

i g n o r e   _____ _____

Review

When words follow the VC/CV pattern and there is only one middle consonant sound, the consonant is doubled.

2 Fill in the missing letters. Then say the word as you write each syllable.

connive   co____ ____ive   _____ _____

collide   co____ ___ide   _____ _____

oppose   o____ ___ose   _____ _____

suppose   su____ ___ose   _____ _____

commune   co____ ___une   _____ _____

accuse   a____ ___use   _____ _____

pollute   po____ ___ute   _____ _____

immune   i___ ___une   _____ _____

3 **QUICK CHECK** Have another student test you on spelling these words.

My score: _____/_____ words correct

(1) Directions:

• Your teacher will dictate ten two-syllable words.

• Repeat the word.

• Isolate and pronounce each syllable, saying the sounds as you spell.

• Combine the syllables and say the whole word as you write it.

1. ☐☐ _____

2. ☐☐ _____

3. ☐☐ _____

4. ☐☐ _____

5. ☐☐ _____

6. ☐☐ _____

7. ☐☐ _____

8. ☐☐ _____

9. ☐☐ _____

10. ☐☐ _____

1 **Draw a line to match each word to its definition.**

accuse	to become stale and inactive
explore	to say someone did something wrong
advice	to travel in an unknown area
reptile	to take away
connive	a thin, soft layer of plant or animal tissue
stagnate	hints or tips to help someone with a problem
confiscate	to work together secretly
membrane	a snake, lizard, or turtle

Proofreading Practice

Two of the List 3 words are misspelled in each of the sentences. Cross out each misspelled word, and write the correct spelling above it.

1. Good athletes try not to dispute when they colide by misteak.

2. Do you suppose the umpire will retir after he compleats his contract?

3. We'll invite the intire cast to a costoom party after the show.

4. Did the actors compensaet the retired man after they envaided his home?

5. As Dan discribs the landscape near the old estate, Lena ilostrates it.

6. The children consoom a lot of pancakes, and then they exuze themselves.

1 **Fill in the blanks with words from the box.**

umpire	reptile	stampeded	tadpole
inclined	opposed	empire	membrane
stagnate	inquired	confiscate	connive

1. The mucous _____ is in your nose.

2. The water in the pond will _____ unless the dam is opened.

3. The _____ grew into a frog.

4. Our class spent all our time at the zoo in the _____ house

   watching the snakes.

5. The _____ called the ball a foul.

6. The horses _____ when they heard the gunshot.

7. She _____ about a room in the hotel.

8. The two teams _____ each other on the playing field.

9. The customs officer will _____ the fruit from the tourists.

10. The bandits will _____ to rob the bank.

11. Many countries were once part of the Roman _____.

12. Patrick is not _____ to try out for the football team.

   He loves basketball.

1 Complete the puzzle with words from the box.

reptile	extreme	inflate	accuse	empire
concrete	dispute	infantile	trombone	dictate
intrude	textile	escape	collide	

Across

3. a large brass musical instrument
4. to blow up with air
5. like a baby
8. to say or read aloud for someone else to write down
11. argue, debate
12. a cold-blooded animal that creeps or crawls
13. a mixture of cement, sand, and water
14. to run away

Down

1. to rush against; to bump into
2. to force oneself on others without being asked or wanted
6. to charge with having done something wrong
7. a group of countries that follow one leader
9. woven fabric
10. very great; very strong; at the very end

(1) **Read the sentences and circle all the List 3 words.**

1. It is hard not to collide with other swimmers when doing the backstroke.

2. The athlete hurt his backbone by jogging on concrete.

3. I advise you to compare prices before you subscribe to this newspaper.

4. Arnell admired the sunrise in the landscape.

5. Don't confuse me anymore with your advice.

6. Watching the sunrise is one of my favorite pastimes.

7. If we do not enclose the horses in a pen, they may stampede.

8. Justin made a mistake when he computed that problem.

9. It would be insane to eat 100 pancakes.

10. The fans will dispute the umpire's call.

(2) **Your teacher will dictate three of the sentences above. Write them on a blank piece of paper.**

(3) **Write a short story or descriptive paragraph using ten words from List 3. Be creative!**

Reading & Spelling Skill Check

Demonstrate your accuracy in reading and spelling List 3 words. Your teacher will select ten words to read and ten words to spell. Record your scores on the Accuracy Checklist. Work toward 90–100 percent accuracy.

Word Proficiency

Now build up your reading proficiency with List 3 words. Decide on your rate goal with your teacher. Record your progress on the Word Proficiency Graph.

My goal for reading List 3 is _____ words per minute with two or fewer errors.

1 Practice the words, read the passage, and then answer the questions.

List 3 Words			Review Words	Passage Words	
concluded	sunshine	dispute	problem(s)	dying	warming
extreme	infiltrate	exposed	daytime	scientists	temperature(s)
membrane	ignore	concrete		global	thirty

Why Are the Frogs Dying?

For the past thirty years, frogs have been dying out. For a long time, the problem left scientists confused. Now they think they have found the cause: global warming.

Global warming means the world's temperature is going up. Temperatures don't have to be extreme to hurt frogs. A frog's skin is a thin membrane. Just a small temperature change can cause huge problems. Global warming causes clouds to block out sunshine, which makes temperatures go down in the daytime and up at night. These temperatures help a fungus, or growth, infiltrate the frogs' skin. Frogs exposed to this fungus get sick and die.

The good news is that scientists now have concrete proof that global warming makes real problems. No one can ignore it or dispute it any more. If global warming can be stopped, then the dying frogs can one day be saved.

1. What word from the text means "get inside"? _____

2. What happened as temperatures went up in places where the frogs lived? _____

_____

3. Why might the news of the dying frogs be a good thing? _____

_____

2 FLUENCY Record your progress on the Fluency Graph.

My goal for reading the passage is _____ words per minute with two or fewer errors.

-*er*- = /er/			-*ar*- = /ar/	-*or*- = /or/	-*ur*- = /er/ -*ir*- = /er/
adverb	manner	slipper	artist	absorb	absurd
anger	master	suffer	barber	afford	burden
berserk	matter	summer	carbon	border	circle
better	member	supper	carcass	corner	circus
bitter	monster	temper	carpet	correct	confirm
butler	number	tender	darling	Cory	curfew
butter	offer	thunder	discard	distort	current
chapter	pamper	timber	farmer	endorse	curtsy
chatter	pattern	under	farther	enforce	disturb
copper	pepper	verbal	garden	escort	flirted
differ	perfect	verdict	garlic	export	furnish
dinner	perfume	vermin	garment	forbid	further
enter	perhaps	Vermont	garter	forceps	murder
expert	permit	versus	hardly	forest	murmur
fender	persist	whisper	harness	horrid	occur
finger	person	winter	harvest	import	perturb
gather	Peter	zipper	jargon	inform	squirrel
hammer	rather		market	morbid	squirted
hermit	Robert		parcel	mortal	surplus
hunger	rubber		pardon	orbit	surprise
ladder	serpent		parsnip	order	thirsty
lantern	servant		partner	organ	turban
letter	sherbet		party	orphan	turkey
lobster	silver		tardy	perform	turnip
lumber	slender		target	torment	urban

Three-Syllable Words:

abnormal	carpenter	informal	permanent	Ariel	different
interrupt	turpentine	Armando	important	Lorenzo	

The *r*-Controlled Syllable (V*r*)

The **r-controlled syllable (Vr)** has a vowel followed by an *r*. The vowel sound is neither long nor short.

You have to learn these V*r* combinations and their sounds.

ar	says /ar/ as in	*car*	
or	says /or/ as in	*fort*	
er	says /er/ as in	*fern*	
ir	says /er/ as in	*bird*	} These all have the same sound: /er/.
ur	says /er/ as in	*turn*	

1 Circle the V*r* combination in each word. Then write the words under the correct headings, according to their sounds.

p e r t	d a r n	c u r t	t a r p
f i r m	s i r	f o r	h e r
t a r	w o r n	s t e r n	s t o r k
p o r t	b u r n	c h a r t	s h i r t

/ar/   **/or/**

_____ _____

_____ _____

_____ _____

_____ _____

/er/

_____ _____

_____ _____

_____ _____

_____ _____

1 Circle the *r*-controlled syllables.

vir	tle	lish	curf	nee	cass
tern	tar	thir	par	ber	bine
mit	poin	per	sume	turb	sorb
surd	sher	mur	squir	la	cir
gar	dar	vi	nor	tort	cort

2 Write the *r*-controlled syllables above under the correct headings. Then read the syllables to another student.

/ar/ as in *car*

_____

_____

_____

_____

/or/ as in *fort*

_____

_____

_____

_____

/er/ as in *fern*

_____

_____

_____

_____

/er/ as in *bird*

_____

_____

_____

_____

/er/ as in *turn*

_____

_____

_____

_____

⟲ *Review*

A **closed syllable** has _____ vowel and ends in a _____.

A **silent-*e* syllable** has a vowel-_____-*e.*

An ***r*-controlled syllable** has a vowel followed by an _____.

A **closed syllable** has a _____ vowel sound.

A **silent-*e* syllable** has a _____ vowel sound.

Which syllable has neither a short- nor a long-vowel sound? _____

---

① Write the syllables under the correct headings. Then read them to another student.

nish	tal	fen	ur	lete	cus
ler	tane	plode	es	mon	lide
cuse	ster	sist	lute	thun	tort
sur	trive	tern	car	pur	sume

Closed Syllables (VC)	Silent-*e* Syllables (VCe)	*r*-Controlled Syllables (V*r*)
_____	_____	_____
_____	_____	_____
_____	_____	_____
_____	_____	_____
_____	_____	_____
_____	_____	_____
_____	_____	_____
_____	_____	_____

/er/

The three possible spellings for /er/ are *er, ir,* and *ur.*

(1) Your teacher will dictate ten *r*-controlled syllables. Say each syllable as you write it.

1. _____
2. _____
3. _____
4. _____
5. _____

6. _____
7. _____
8. _____
9. _____
10. _____

Review

Underline the correct word in the parentheses.

A closed syllable has a (short, long, neither) vowel sound.

A silent-*e* syllable has a (short, long, neither) vowel sound.

An *r*-controlled syllable has (short, long, neither).

(2) Your teacher will dictate fifteen syllables. Listen for the vowel sound, and write the syllables under the correct headings.

Closed Syllables	Silent-*e* Syllables	*r*-Controlled Syllables
_____	_____	_____
_____	_____	_____
_____	_____	_____
_____	_____	_____
_____	_____	_____

1 Circle the *r*-controlled pattern(s). Say the syllables to read the whole word. Then draw a line between the syllables as shown.

but	(ler)	but	ler	sher	bet	s h e r b e t
mur	mur	m u r m u r	ab	surd	a b s u r d
ad	verb	a d v e r b	dis	turb	d i s t u r b
tur	ban	t u r b a n	bur	den	b u r d e n

2 Match the syllables to make real words. Say each word as you write it.

per	cort	_perhaps_	ham	vest	_____
num	cus	_____	squir	mer	_____
cir	ber	_____	har	form	_____
es	haps	_____	per	rel	_____

gar	ster	_____	car	surd	_____
mon	rent	_____	per	pet	_____
mur	lic	_____	tur	son	_____
cur	mur	_____	ab	nip	_____

3 Unscramble the syllables to make a real word.

por	im	tant	_____
in	rupt	ter	_____
ter	pen	car	_____
fer	dif	ent	_____
nor	mal	ab	_____
pen	tur	tine	_____
mal	for	in	_____

Spelling Patterns

The pattern *per* is a common spelling for /per/ at the beginning of words.

(1) **Fill in the missing syllable *per*. Then write the whole words next to the correct definitions.**

___*per*___ fume   **1.** allowing to do something   _____

_____ fect   **2.** lasting   _____

_____ mit   **3.** without fault   _____

_____ sist   **4.** trouble greatly   _____

_____ turb   **5.** sweet-smelling liquid   ___*perfume*___

_____ ma nent **6.** refuse to stop   _____

The pattern *ver* is common in multisyllabic words.

(2) **Fill in the missing letters *ver*. Then write the whole words next to the correct definitions.**

_____ sus   **1.** decision of a jury   _____

_____ min   **2.** northeastern U.S. state   _____

_____ dict   **3.** part of speech   _____

ad _____ b   **4.** against   _____

_____ mont   **5.** fleas, lice, rats, and bedbugs _____

The pattern *tur* is a common spelling for /ter/ in multisyllabic words.

(3) **Fill in the missing letters *tur*. Then write the whole words next to the correct definitions.**

_____ nip   **1.** scarf worn around the head   _____

per _____ b   **2.** used to thin paint   _____

_____ ban   **3.** large bird   _____

_____ key   **4.** trouble greatly   _____

_____ pen tine **5.** type of vegetable   _____

/er/ at the end of words is most often spelled with *er*.

(1) **Read the clues. Fill in the missing syllable with *er*, and then write the whole word.**

talk softly	whis_____	_____
a metal	sil_____	_____
comes after fall	win_____	_____
opposite of over	un_____	_____
to go in	en_____	_____
one of five on each hand	fin_____	_____
a type of shellfish	lob_____	_____
part of a book	chap_____	_____
a need for food	hun_____	_____
logs, boards	lum_____	_____
feeling mad	an_____	_____
32 is one	num_____	_____
front part of a car	fen_____	_____
state of mind	tem_____	_____
slim	slen_____	_____
the noise heard in storms	thun_____	_____
to bring together	gath_____	_____

(2) **EXCEPTION Practice these exceptions.**

occur   murmur

occ ____ ____   murm ____ ____

_____   _____

1 Your teacher will dictate sixteen words. Spell the missing syllable. Then say the whole word as you write it.

1. _____ den   _____

2. _____ son   _____

3. _____ ner   _____

4. _____ ner   _____

5. _____ dict   _____

6. _____ key   _____

7. chap _____   _____

8. mur _____   _____

9. fur _____   _____

10. dis _____   _____

11. sil _____   _____

12. ex _____   _____

13. bar _____   _____

14. _____ pen _____   _____

15. dif _____ ent   _____

16. im _____ tant   _____

Review

Draw a line to match the name of the syllable to its code.

Closed Syllable   V*r*

Silent-*e* Syllable   VC

r-Controlled Syllable   VC*e*

ⓢ *Review*

VC/CV Syllabication Rule: When two or more _____

stand between two _____, you divide between the

_____ so that blends and digraphs stay together.

① Draw a line to divide the words into syllables. Then write the words under the correct headings below.

enforce	burden	absurd	sherbet	verdict
jargon	different	forceps	curfew	orbit
interrupt	turpentine	urban	berserk	informal
perturb	escort	absorb	important	carpenter

Two-Syllable Words

_____ _____

_____ _____

_____ _____

_____ _____

_____ _____

_____ _____

_____ _____

Three-Syllable Words

_____ _____

_____ _____

_____ _____

1 Circle the *r*-controlled combinations in the words below. Then write the words under the correct headings.

perfect   squirrel   disturb   interrupt   murmur

person   thunder   serpent   servant   permit

surprise turkey   burden   differ   squirted

circus   perfume   hunger   furnish   whisper

er Words	*ur* Words	*ir* Words
_____	_____	_____
_____	_____	_____
_____	_____	_____
_____	_____	
_____	_____	
_____	_____	
_____		
_____		
_____		
_____		
_____		

2 **QUICK CHECK** Have another student test you on spelling these words.

My score: _____ /_____ words correct

Review

Three ways to spell /er/ are _____, _____,

and _____.

Review

Underline the correct words in parentheses.

Double Middle Consonant Spelling Rule: In a two-syllable word, when you hear *(no, one)* consonant sound after the first *(short, long)* vowel sound, double the *(consonant, vowel)*.

(1) Fill in the missing letters. Then say the syllables aloud as you write the whole word.

not sweet, nor sour	bi ____ ____ er	_____
used to pound nails	ha ____ ____ er	_____
small animal that eats acorns	squi ____ ____ el	_____
comes after spring	su ____ ____ er	_____
evening meal	su ____ ____ er	_____
evening meal	di ____ ____ er	_____
spread on bread	bu ____ ____ er	_____
type of metal	co ____ ____ er	_____
used to climb	la ____ ____ er	_____
disagree	di ____ ____ er	_____
light, low shoe	sli ____ ____ er	_____
_____ band	ru ____ ____ er	_____
to feel pain	su ____ ____ er	_____
mail	le ____ ____ er	_____
something that zips	zi ____ ____ er	_____
good, _____, best	be ____ ____ er	_____

(2) **QUICK CHECK** Have another student test you on spelling some of these words.

My score: _____ /_____ words correct

At the end of words, *on, an,* and *en* all spell /ən/.

1 Circle *on, an,* or *en* in these words. Then write the words under the correct headings.

person   orphan   burden   carbon   pardon

jargon   garden   urban   organ   turban

an Words	*on* Words	*en* Words
_____	_____	_____
_____	_____	_____
_____	_____	
_____		

At the end of words, *et* and *it* spell /ət/ or /ĭt/.

2 Circle *et* or *it* in these words. Then write the words under the correct headings.

market   hermit   target

orbit   permit   sherbet

et Words	*it* Words
_____	_____
_____	_____
_____	_____

3 **QUICK CHECK** Have another student test you on spelling some of these words.

My score: _____ /_____ words correct

Proofreading Practice

Two of the List 4 words are misspelled in each of the sentences. Rewrite the whole sentence, and spell the words correctly.

1. The carpanter's hammer, the farmar's rake, or the artist's knife could have been used to prop open the window.

_____

_____

2. Morris served lobster, bread with garlic buttor, and sherbet for super.

_____

_____

3. If the children wisper and chatter, they will disturb everyone at the orgen concert.

_____

_____

4. When Peter saw the sirpant move unnder his chair, he went berserk.

_____

_____

5. Perhaps the cook will oferr to make terkey with garlic sauce for dinner tonight.

_____

_____

6. Is it a suprize that winter and summer difer from each other?

_____

_____

7. Marla was thersty at the party, so she asked her eskorrt for a glass of water.

_____

1 **Fill in the blanks with words from the box.**

partner	squirrels	correct	gather	chapter	furnish
further	order	barber	permit	lantern	perfect
matter	perfume	carpenter	organ	important	artist

1. Walter has to finish reading _____ five for history

   class tomorrow.

2. The wind was strong, so it was a _____ day to go sailing.

3. The _____ will cut your hair at 10:00 a.m.

4. How much _____ do we have to go?

5. My business _____ made an _____

   sale today.

6. Before a _____ can begin work on the house, you will need

   a building _____.

7. _____ your things so we can leave now.

8. Doris smells nice. She is wearing a new kind of _____.

9. The _____ were making a lot of noise scampering from tree

   to tree.

10. Does it _____ if we're ten minutes late?

11. The _____ sold his paintings at the fair.

12. We want to _____ the house with new chairs. We will have to

    _____ them from the store.

13. The teacher has many tests to _____ before class.

14. Because it's so dark tonight, we should put a _____ out

    on the patio.

15. The class went to hear Victor play the _____ at the church.

1 **Replace the underlined words with a word from the box. Write the word on the line.**

pamper	hermit	mortals	perturb	jargon	vermin
absurd	murmur	endorse	urban	carcass	parcels

1. When I'm sick, I like to have someone <u>give lots of attention to</u> me.

    _____

2. Carmen could hear the <u>soft, low sound</u> of voices in the next room.

    _____

3. There is a great need for more <u>city</u> housing.

    _____

4. Martin lives in a shack in the woods. People call him a <u>person who goes away from other people to live by himself.</u>

    _____

5. Doctors use a lot of <u>special words</u> that most people don't understand.

    _____

6. Ginger found the <u>dead body</u> of a deer in the forest.

    _____

7. People are <u>beings that are sure to die sometime.</u>

    _____

8. Norman's plan to hitchhike to Vermont is <u>foolish and unreasonable.</u>

    _____

9. Victor had his arms filled with <u>packages and gifts.</u>

    _____

10. Don't forget to <u>write your name on the back of</u> the check before you put it into the bank.

    _____

11. These prank phone calls greatly <u>trouble</u> me.

    _____

12. We found lots of <u>fleas, rats, and bugs</u> in the rundown shack.

    _____

(1) **Read the sentences and circle all the List 4 words.**

1. During the summer, the weather is almost perfect in Vermont.

2. The jury reached a verdict of guilty in the murder case.

3. Walter will plant turnips and parsnips in his garden this year.

4. We must whisper so that we don't disturb the person in the next room.

5. The expert carpenter needs more lumber and a ladder before she builds the house.

6. The United States imports rubber and exports its surplus wheat.

7. Arnell will furnish the punch for the surprise dinner party.

8. The squirrel ran up the tree when the thunder started.

9. The lobster pinched the servant's finger.

10. Martin wants to order garlic bread for supper.

(2) **Your teacher will dictate three of the sentences above. Write them on a blank piece of paper.**

(3) **Write a short story or descriptive paragraph using ten words from List 4. Be creative!**

✓ Reading & Spelling Skill Check

Demonstrate your accuracy in reading and spelling List 4 words. Your teacher will select ten words to read and ten words to spell. Record your scores on the Accuracy Checklist. Work toward 90–100 percent accuracy.

Word Proficiency

Now build up your reading proficiency with List 4 words. Decide on your rate goal with your teacher. Record your progress on the Word Proficiency Graph.

My goal for reading List 4 is _____ words per minute with two or fewer errors.

1 Practice the words, read the passage, and then answer the questions.

List 4 Words			Review Words		Passage Words
Ariel	lumber	ladder	actress	something	handy
theater	fingers	murmur(ed)		admire	building
summer	master	Cory			
hammer	carpenter				

Told You

Ariel was working at a theater for the summer. She was a good actress, and she was handy with a hammer, too.

Cory, the theater owner, asked Ariel to help build the set. They started by building a wall with shelves.

Cory watched as Ariel sawed pieces of lumber. "Watch your fingers!" he said, but Ariel was a master carpenter and great with a handsaw. Once the wall was up, Cory carried wood up a ladder to nail the shelves to the wall.

As Cory came down the ladder, Ariel saw something odd. "You need more nails or those shelves will fall," she said.

"Don't worry, kid," murmured Cory. "I know what I'm doing."

Once the shelves were done, Ariel and Cory loaded them with canned goods. They stood back to admire their work, and they heard a crack as the shelves came crashing down.

"Told you," Ariel said, as she smiled and turned to the side.

"Okay," Cory said, throwing his hands up. "You were right."

1. What word from the text means "said quietly"? _____

2. What did Ariel think was wrong with how Cory put up the shelves? _____

_____

3. Why did Cory tell Ariel she was right? _____

_____

2 **FLUENCY** Decide on your fluency rate goal with your teacher. Record your progress on the Fluency Graph.

My goal for reading the passage is _____ words per minute with two or fewer errors.

actress	compare	explore	peanut
address	compute	finger	pollute
advice	concrete	forest	popcorn
afternoon	confuse	forget	rabbit
baseball	contest	garden	seldom
bottom	dentist	headache	sidewalk
carpet	dinner	hundred	summer
children	escape	invite	surprise
circle	everything	member	temper
classroom	excuse	mistake	tonight
collect	expert	notebook	traffic

1 Write the words under the correct headings.

garden	traffic	member
contest	compute	summer
advice	excuse	bottom

VC/CV Closed Syllables	VC/CV Closed and Silent-*e* Syllables	VC/CV Closed and *r*-Controlled Syllables
_____	_____	_____
_____	_____	_____
_____	_____	_____

2 Fill in the blanks with compound words from the box.

afternoon	baseball	everything	popcorn
sidewalk	tonight	forget	classroom
headache	notebook	peanut	

1. How could you _____ your own birthday?

2. Sam hit a home run in yesterday's _____ game.

3. The fireworks were so loud that Mom had a _____ afterward.

4. When we leave school this _____, make sure I have

   my _____.

5. Pete and Kim shared some _____ at the movie theater.

6. Do you have _____ you need for our camping trip?

7. Be sure to stay on the _____ until it is safe to cross the street.

8. I'm going to have a _____ butter sandwich for lunch today.

9. We're lucky that our _____ is close to the cafeteria.

10. I hope we don't have too much homework to do _____.

3 Match the word parts to make real words. Then say each word as you write it.

ad	noon	*advice*
cir	tress	_____
after	dress	_____
ad	cle	_____
ac	vice	_____

den	pert	_____
mis	est	_____
ex	tist	_____
for	thing	_____
every	take	_____

4 Underline the word that is spelled correctly.

1. If you leave the gate open, the dog might (escap, escape).

2. How many (children, childrin) are there in your family?

3. Dad and I watched a (basball, baseball) game last night.

4. Jess wants to (invite, invit) everyone in the class to her birthday party.

5. (Summer, Summir) is the best season of the year.

6. Every (membur, member) of my family loves to swim.

7. There's a great prize if you win the (contest, conntest).

8. Grandfather is coming to visit (tunnite, tonight).

9. Over and over, the robot repeated, "That does not (compute, comput)."

10. There is no good (excuse, excues) for hurting an animal.

5 Complete the puzzle with the words from the box.

bottom	headache	notebook	traffic	confuse	pollute
carpet	collect	hundred	forget	seldom	rabbit
concrete	explore	temper	classroom	compare	

Across
1. to gather things together
3. the movement of cars and trucks along roads
4. a pain in the head
6. to cause harm to the environment
10. the lowest part of something
11. a mixture of cement, sand, and water
13. not often
14. to look for similarities
15. the number after 99: one _____

Down
1. a thick fabric covering a floor
2. a room in a school
3. a tendency to get angry easily
5. an animal that hops
7. to search or investigate
8. to mistake one thing for another
9. a book with paper for writing
12. the opposite of *remember*

/ā/	/ē/	/ī/	/ō/	/ū/ and /ōō/
agent	decent	bison	bonus	brutal
baby	decide	cider	donate	Cuban
bacon	deduct	climax	holy	Cupid
basic	ego	fiber	hotel	duty
basin	elope	final	local	human
blazer	equal	iris	locate	humid
crater	erase	Irish	moment	music
crazy	even	item	omit	puny
gravy	event	ivy	open	pupil
halo	evil	lilac	polo	putrid
Jason	female	minus	pony	student
label	fever	pilot	rodent	super
lady	frequent	rival	Roman	Susan
later	hero	silent	rotate	tulip
lazy	legal	siren	slogan	tuna
navy	meter	spider	sloping	tunic
paper	recent	spiral	sober	unit
raven	secret	tidy	solo	unite
Stacey	Steven	tiger	spoken	
vacant	Venus	tiny	toga	
	veto	virus	total	
	zero	vital	totem	
			trophy	

Practice Page **5A**

The Open Syllable (CV)

An **open syllable (CV)** ends in a vowel. The vowel is usually long *(lō, crā)*.

1 Read these open syllables aloud to practice the long vowel sounds. Some are nonsense syllables, and some are real words.

de	be	bru	so	ve
fi	I	hi	ti	go
she	tu	fro	slo	pi
hu	fre	me	we	tro
pro	va	na	flu	cu

2 Write five real words from the list above.

_____

_____

_____

_____

_____

3 Now your teacher will dictate five open syllables. Say each syllable as you write it.

1. _____

2. _____

3. _____

4. _____

5. _____

Review

Draw a line to match each syllable to the type of syllable.

ter   Closed syllable (VC)

trom   Silent-*e* syllable (VC*e*)

lide   *r*-Controlled syllable (V*r*)

1 Write the syllables under the correct headings. Then read them aloud.

la	ber	nus	lope	cate	male
ter	so	dent	tem	dy	rase
ris	e	fi	per	ser	der
spo	vil	ru	lent	cret	nate

Open (CV)	Closed (VC)	Silent-*e* (VC*e*)	*r*-Controlled (V*r*)
_____	_____	_____	_____
_____	_____	_____	_____
_____	_____	_____	_____
_____	_____	_____	_____
_____	_____	_____	_____
_____	_____		
_____	_____		

2 Your teacher will dictate nine syllables. Repeat each syllable, and write it under the correct heading.

Open (CV)	Closed (VC)	Silent-*e* (VC*e*)	*r*-Controlled (V*r*)
_____	_____	_____	_____
_____	_____	_____	
_____	_____		

Practice Page **5c**

V/CV Syllabication Rule

When one consonant is surrounded by two vowels, you usually divide the word into syllables before the consonant. The first syllable is open, so the vowel sound is long.

(1) Mark the first vowel long (ˉ). Say the syllables to read the whole word. Then draw a line to divide the syllables as shown.

crā	zy	cra|zy	he	ro	h e r o
I	rish	I r i s h	i	ris	i r i s
fe	male	f e m a l e	pu	ny	p u n y
hu	man	h u m a n	cra	ter	c r a t e r
ha	lo	h a l o	u	nite	u n i t e
u	nit	u n i t	pi	lot	p i l o t

(2) Match the syllables to make real words. Then say each word as you write it.

i	ven	_ivy_____	bru	bot	_____
ra	vy	_____	le	tal	_____
e	mid	_____	ba	con	_____
hu	ven	_____	ro	gal	_____
e	nal	_____	se	dent	_____
va	tal	_____	stu	ver	_____
fi	vil	_____	slo	gan	_____
to	cant	_____	fe	cret	_____

(3) Write *open* or *closed* to complete the definitions.

1. A(n) _____ syllable ends in one vowel. The vowel is usually long.

2. A(n) _____ syllable has one vowel, ends in a consonant, and has a short-vowel sound.

1 Your teacher will dictate twelve words. Spell the missing syllable. Then say the whole word as you write it.

1. _____ ven   _____

2. _____ zy   _____

3. _____ cate   _____

4. _____ ty   _____

5. _____ nal   _____

6. po _____   _____

7. bo _____   _____

8. fe _____   _____

9. la _____   _____

10. spi _____   _____

11. fe _____   _____

12. ho _____   _____

Review

V/CV Syllabication Rule: When a single _____ is surrounded

by two _____, you divide the word into syllables before the

_____. This makes the first syllable _____

and the vowel sound _____.

The Schwa Sound

Many V/CV words have a schwa sound (/ə/) in the unaccented second syllable. The accent in a two-syllable word is usually on the first syllable, so the second syllable has the schwa sound.

/əl/ at the end of some V/CV words is often spelled *al*.

(1) **Read the clues, and fill in the missing letters *al*. Then write the whole word.**

at the end; the last   fi n_____   _____

having to do with a certain place   lo c_____   _____

the same amount   e qu_____   _____

having to do with the law   le g_____   _____

one who tries to outdo another   ri v_____   _____

whole; entire   to t_____   _____

a winding coil   spi r_____   _____

having to do with life   vi t_____   _____

(2) **EXCEPTION** **Practice these exceptions.**

la bel   e vil   pu pil

la b___ ___   e v___ ___   pu p___ ___

_____   _____   _____

/ənt/ at the end of some V/CV words is often spelled *ent*.

(3) **Fill in the missing letters *ent*, and then write the whole word.**

a g_____   _____   re c_____   _____

fre qu_____   _____   si l_____   _____

stu d_____   _____   ro d_____   _____

(4) **QUICK CHECK** **Have another student test you on spelling these words.**

My score: _____/_____ words correct

Review

To spell /ən/ at the end of two-syllable words, choose one of these spellings:

on as in *ribbon*   *in* as in *napkin*

en as in *kitten*   *an* as in *urban*

(1) **Circle the last two letters in each of the following V/CV words. Then write the words under the correct headings.**

even   basin   open   raven

human   slogan   bison   siren

spoken   bacon   Steven   Susan

an	**en**	**in**
_____	_____	_____
_____	_____	**on**
_____	_____	_____
	_____	_____
	_____	

/əd/ at the end of words is sometimes spelled *id*.

(2) **Read the clues, and spell the missing syllable with *id*. Then write the whole word.**

1. smells bad; rotten   pu_____   _____

2. hot and muggy   hu_____   _____

3. the god of love   Cu_____   _____

Practice Page 5G

These words follow the V/CV Syllabication Rule. You divide the syllables after the first vowel, and that vowel is long. The second vowel may be schwa, long, short, silent-*e*, or *r*-controlled. The accent is on the first syllable of most two-syllable words.

(1) Draw a line to divide between the syllables, and mark the first vowel long. Write the first (accented) syllable in the box and the second (unaccented) syllable on the blank line.

b a s i n ☐ _____   l o c a t e ☐ _____

h e r o ☐ _____   t o t e m ☐ _____

t i d y ☐ _____   e q u a l ☐ _____

t o t a l ☐ _____   c r a t e r ☐ _____

C u p i d ☐ _____   l e g a l ☐ _____

s l o g a n ☐ _____   b a s i c ☐ _____

m e t e r ☐ _____   e v i l ☐ _____

b r u t a l ☐ _____   l a z y ☐ _____

p i l o t ☐ _____   u n i t ☐ _____

(2) Now fill in the blanks to describe the words in Activity 1.

The first syllable is always _____ and the vowel sound is always

_____ .

1 Circle the spelling that looks right to you, and check your answers at the bottom of the page. Then write the correct spelling on the blank line.

bacan or (bacon?) _____bacon_____

pilot or pilet? _____

total or totil? _____

humen or human? _____

unet or unit? _____

label or labil? _____

secrit or secret? _____

final or finel? _____

itum or item? _____

evin or even? _____

open or opin? _____

frequint or frequent? _____

2 **QUICK CHECK** Have another student test you on these words.

My score: _____ / _____ words correct

Proofreading Practice

Two of the List 5 words are misspelled in each of the sentences. Cross out each misspelled word, and write the correct spelling above it.

1. The vet on duty said that high feaver and a virus caused the tigger's death.

2. The secret ajent tried to locait the legal papers in the forest.

3. Stacey put a lable on each iris and toolip in the tidy garden.

ANSWERS: bacon, pilot, total, human, unit, label, secret, final, item, even, open, frequent

1 Your teacher will dictate ten words. Write the accented syllable in the box and the unaccented syllable on the short line. Then write the whole word.

1. [ ] _____ _____

2. [ ] _____ _____

3. [ ] _____ _____

4. [ ] _____ _____

5. _____ [ ] _____

6. [ ] _____ _____

7. [ ] _____ _____

8. [ ] _____ _____

9. [ ] _____ _____

10. [ ] _____ _____

(1) **Fill in the blanks with words from the box.**

lilac	music	decide	tuna	super
Navy	tulip	solo	local	basic
cider	trophy	rotates	deduct	event
iris	crater	polo	secret	agent

1. A lake had formed in the _____ of the volcano.

2. Lucy can _____ the cost of child care when she pays her taxes.

3. Stacey and Steven's wedding was a splendid _____.

4. The earth _____ on its axis.

5. Susan is a great athlete. She helped her team win a _____ at

   the _____ match.

6. Since the _____ store does not have any apple

   _____, we will have to drive to one farther away.

7. Ruby bought a can of _____ fish at the

   _____market.

8. In the school's year-end _____ show, Rosa sang a

   _____.

9. Jonah and Dale joined the _____ and took

   _____ training together.

10. I cannot _____ which flower I like best—the

    _____, the _____, or the

    _____.

11. A _____ _____ spies for a country.

① Read the words. Choose the correct opposite from the box, and write it on the line.

pupil	evil	tidy	brutal	sloping
omit	female	open	lazy	minus
even	tiny	~~lady~~	silent	later

gentleman _____ lady _____

good _____

include _____

big _____

closed _____

noisy, loud _____

odd _____

sooner _____

kind, gentle _____

teacher _____

male _____

messy _____

hard-working _____

flat, even _____

plus _____

1 Complete the puzzle with words from the box.

crater	tulip	recent	raven	puny
virus	rodent	hotel	spider	equal
tuna	trophy	baby	veto	final

Across
1. something that makes you sick
3. a bug with eight legs
6. not long ago
8. to stop a bill from becoming a law
10. a place to stay away from home
11. a flower that grows from a bulb
13. an infant
14. a large, black bird

Down
2. a rat, a mouse, or a squirrel
4. a prize
5. the last; at the end
7. a large, round space on the surface of a planet or moon
9. when two things are the same
11. a fish that many people eat
12. small and weak

(1) **Read the sentences and circle all the List 5 words.**

    1. The Romans often wore togas and tunics.

    2. At the zoo, Jason saw a pony, three tigers, and four bison.

    3. The secret agent spent the night in the tiny hotel.

    4. Cupid and Venus are the god and goddess of love.

    5. The hotel clerk is not on duty tonight because he has a virus and a fever.

    6. Owen read about an Irish hero.

    7. Ten minus ten equals zero.

    8. The label was printed on silver paper.

    9. The baby would stop crying the moment we played music.

  10. Lucy will donate some cash to her best music students.

  11. Can the president veto the bill on equal rights?

(2) **Your teacher will dictate three of the sentences above. Write them on a blank piece of paper.**

(3) **Write a short story or a descriptive paragraph using ten words from List 5. Be creative!**

✓ Reading & Spelling Skill Check

Demonstrate your accuracy in reading and spelling List 5 words. Your teacher will select ten words to read and ten words to spell. Record your scores on the Accuracy Checklist. Work toward 90–100 percent accuracy.

Word Proficiency

Now build up your reading proficiency with List 5 words. Decide on your rate goal with your teacher. Record your progress on the Word Proficiency Graph.

    My goal for reading List 5 is _____ words per minute with two or fewer errors.

1 Practice the words, read the passage, and then answer the questions.

List 5 Words			Review Words	Passage Words	
tiger(s)	zero	vital	number	Asia	reserves
trophy	even	humans	compete	people	protects
brutal	basic			Project	resources
total	donate			India	

Hope for Wild Tigers

Did you know that there are more tigers in zoos than there are wild tigers all over the world? There are fewer than 5,000 tigers left in the wild. But what happened to the wild tigers, and why are there so few left?

Tigers live in Asia, where the number of humans has grown fast. Tigers cannot compete with humans for food and land. People hunt and kill tigers, too. A tiger skin is a trophy for brutal hunters. In your lifetime, the total number of tigers in the wild could be zero.

There is hope for tigers. Project Tiger, in India, is fighting to save the tigers. Project Tiger sets up large wildlife reserves for tigers. The group even protects tigers from hunters. Thanks to Project Tiger, the number of wild tigers may start to grow.

You can join the fight to save wild tigers, too. One basic thing you can do is donate time or resources to wildlife groups like Project Tiger. It helps keep their vital work going.

1. What word from the text means "give to a good cause"? _____

2. Why are there so few tigers in the wild? _____

_____

3. Why may there be hope for wild tigers? _____

_____

2 **FLUENCY** Record your progress on the Fluency Graph.

My goal for reading the passage is _____ words per minute with two or fewer errors.

6 VC/V Syllabication Rule

/ă/	/ĕ/	/ĭ/	/ŏ/	/ŭ/
atom	clever	civic	body	punish
cabin	credit	clinic	closet	study
camel	denim	finish	comet	
dragon	desert	limit	comic	
habit	ever	linen	copy	
magic	lemon	mimic	frolic	
panel	level	prison	model	
planet	melon	river	modern	
radish	menu	sliver	novel	
rapid	metal	timid	polish	
salad	method	tribune	product	
static	never	tribute	project	
talent	pedal	visit	proper	
travel	petal	vivid	robin	
valid	present	widow	solid	
vanish	rebel		tonic	
wagon	relic		topic	
	relish		tropic	
	second		volume	
	seven			
	tepid			

Review

A closed syllable ends in a consonant and has a short vowel sound.

An open syllable ends in one vowel and has a long vowel sound.

(1) Write the syllables under the correct headings, and then read each group aloud.

Open Syllables   **Closed Syllables**

ta

tal

_____   _____

pun

pu

_____   _____

trib

tri

_____   _____

me

mel

_____   _____

pres

pre

_____   _____

ro

rob

_____   _____

pla

plan

_____   _____

rel

re

Practice Page 6B

Review

1. A **closed syllable** has one _____, and it _____ in a consonant.

2. A **silent-e syllable** has a _____ - _____ - _____ spelling pattern.

3. An **r-controlled syllable** has a _____ followed by an *r*.

4. An **open syllable** _____ in one vowel.

5. Which two types of syllables have long-vowel sounds?
_____ and _____

1. Write the syllables under the correct headings. Then read them to another student.

| pres | ish | mod | ute | u | ern |
| ume | nov | per | er | ny | une |

Open (CV)	Closed (VC)	Silent-e (VCe)	r-Controlled (Vr)
_____	_____	_____	_____
_____	_____	_____	_____
	_____	_____	_____
	_____		

2. Your teacher will dictate ten syllables. Repeat each syllable, and write it under the correct heading.

Open (CV)	Closed (VC)	Silent-e (VCe)	r-Controlled (Vr)
_____	_____	_____	_____
_____	_____	_____	_____
_____	_____		

VC/V Syllabication Rule

When a single consonant is surrounded by two vowels, try the V/CV Syllabication Rule first. If that doesn't make a real word, divide the syllables *after* the consonant and give the first vowel its short sound.

1 Mark the first vowel short (ˇ). Say the syllables to read the whole word. Then draw a line between the syllables as shown.

tăl	ent	ta l|ent	lev	el	level
at	om	atom	vol	ume	volume
pun	ish	punish	cop	y	copy
trib	une	tribune	den	im	denim
meth	od	method	rel	ic	relic

2 Match the syllables to make real words. Then say each word as you write it.

trav	et	_____	pun	el	_____
rel	el	_____	sol	im	_____
stud	ish	_____	den	id	_____
clos	y	_____	pan	ish	_____

sal	on	_____	riv	ume	_____
lem	ic	_____	top	er	_____
prop	ad	_____	vol	u	_____
com	er	_____	men	ic	_____

sec	id	_____	plan	ish	_____
ped	ond	_____	cop	el	_____
pol	al	_____	van	et	_____
tim	ish	_____	nov	y	_____

/əl/ at the end of words is often spelled *el.*

(1) **Fill in the missing syllable *el,* and then write the whole word.**

cam_____   _____

trav_____   _____

pan_____   _____

lev_____   _____

reb_____   _____

mod_____   _____

nov_____   _____

(2) **EXCEPTION Sometimes /əl/ is spelled *al.* Use the lines below to learn to spell these words.**

met al   met _____   _____

ped al   ped _____   _____

The most common spelling for /er/ at the end of a word is *er.*

(3) **Fill in the missing syllable *er,* and then write the whole word.**

sliv_____   _____

nev_____   _____

clev_____   _____

riv_____   _____

ev_____   _____

prop_____   _____

(4) **QUICK CHECK Have another student test you on spelling these words.**

My score: _____ /_____ words correct

The word endings *ic* and *ish* are common in VC/V words.

1 Add the final syllable *ic* or *ish* to the syllables below to make a real word. Then write the whole words.

mim_____   _____   civ_____   _____

pun_____   _____   rel_____   _____

clin_____   _____   rad_____   _____

pol_____   _____   mag_____   _____

stat_____   _____   ton_____   _____

2 Read the definitions. Choose the correct word from Activity 1, and write it on the line.

copy; make fun of   _____

related to a city   _____

a drink that gives strength   _____

make something smooth or shiny   _____

place to get medical help   _____

at rest; standing still; noise in a radio broadcast _____

unexplained forces   _____

red vegetable   _____

3 **QUICK CHECK** Have another student test you on spelling these words.

My score: _____ /_____ words correct

(1) Add one of these final syllables to each syllable below. Then say the whole word as you write it.

| el | er | ic | ish |

com_____ _____ fin_____ _____

pol_____ _____ clev_____ _____

prop_____ _____ top_____ _____

van_____ _____ lev_____ _____

frol_____ _____ sliv_____ _____

trav_____ _____ nov_____ _____

(2) Read the synonyms. Choose the correct word from Activity 1, and write it on the line.

play _____

new _____

scrap; piece _____

subject _____

end _____

flat _____

smart _____

disappear _____

funny _____

tour _____

shine _____

correct _____

1 Your teacher will dictate sixteen words. Repeat each word, and spell the missing syllable. Then say the whole word as you write it.

1. _____ er   _____

2. _____ on   _____

3. _____ it   _____

4. trav _____   _____

5. _____ al   _____

6. men _____   _____

7. _____ ern   _____

8. rad _____   _____

9. _____ in   _____

10. _____ y   _____

11. bod _____   _____

12. _____ id   _____

13. _____ ad   _____

14. clev _____   _____

15. _____ on   _____

16. mim _____   _____

2 Now choose five words and use them in sentences.

_____

_____

_____

_____

_____

_____

Review

VC/V Syllabication Rule: When a single consonant is surrounded by two vowels, try the V/CV Syllabication Rule first. If that doesn't make a real word, divide the syllables *after* the consonant and give the first vowel its short sound.

(1) Directions:

- Circle the vowels.

- Draw a line between the syllables.

- Mark the vowels with a long (¯), schwa (ə), or short (˘) sign.

răp│ĭd	wagon	atom
menu	rebel	frolic
tribute	vanish	limit
study	copy	credit
denim	visit	salad
volume	melon	punish

(2) Now read the words above to your teacher or another student.

1 Decide whether to divide the word into syllables before the consonant (V/CV Syllabication Rule) or after it (VC/V Syllabication Rule). Draw a line to divide the syllables, and mark the first vowel long (ˉ) or short (˘). Say each word, and write it under the correct heading.

V/CV		VC/V
lilac	lĭl|y	lily
	lī|lac	
	secret	
	second	
	even	
	ever	
	punish	
	puny	
	study	
	student	
	final	
	finish	
	meter	
	metal	
	polo	
	polish	

⑤ Review

To spell /ən/ at the end of two-syllable words, choose one of these spellings:

on   as in   *ribbon*   *in*   as in   *napkin*

en   as in   *kitten*   *an*   as in   *urban*

① Circle the last two letters in each word. Then write the words under the correct heading.

dragon   seven   melon   lemon   cabin

linen   prison   wagon   robin

on   **en**   **in**

_____   _____   _____

_____   _____   _____

_____

_____

_____

② Fill in the blanks with some of the words from above.

Sam is a fire-breathing _____ who loves to eat fruit,

especially _____s and _____s.

Sometimes he visits our _____ in the woods, pulling a

little red _____ behind him. He always wears a blue hat and

a _____ shirt that has _____ buttons

up the front. We look forward to Sam's visits.

③ **QUICK CHECK** Have another student test you on spelling these words.

My score: _____ /_____ words correct

The patterns *et* and *it* both spell /ət/ at the end of two-syllable words.

1 Circle *et* or *it* in the words below. Then write them under the correct heading.

habit   planet   visit   closet   limit   credit

et Words   **it Words**

_____   _____

_____   _____

                                        _____

                                        _____

/əd/ at the end of words is sometimes spelled *id*.

2 Fill in the missing letters *id*. Then write the whole words next to the correct definitions.

rap_____   **1.** slightly warm _____

tim_____   **2.** true   _____

tep_____   **3.** quick, speedy _____

val_____   **4.** hard, firm   _____

sol_____   **5.** shy   _____

3 **QUICK CHECK** Have another student test you on spelling these words.

My score: _____ / _____ words correct

4 **EXCEPTION** Practice these exceptions.

salad   method

sal ____ d   meth ____ d

_____   _____

Practice Page | 6L

(1) **Fill in the blanks with words from the box.**

present	vanish	modern	copy	body
second	product	method	salad	visit
level	magic	robin	solid	study

1. Andrew and Adam would like to share a _____ for lunch.

2. Lashonda has to stay home tonight to _____ for a math test.

3. It is the best _____ we have on the market. You should buy it

   without a _____ thought.

4. I would rather live in a more _____ house. Old homes tend to

   have too many problems.

5. Josh has a foolproof _____ for getting rid of tough stains.

6. The top shelf is not _____. Can you make it flat?

7. They were glad to leave the boat and put their feet on _____

   ground.

8. Kevin knows a lot of _____ tricks.

9. Do you mind if I make a _____ of that photo? I would like to

   send one to Monica.

10. John has a strong, healthy _____. He makes an effort to keep fit.

11. Kristen's birthday is next week. I need to buy her a _____.

12. The _____ is one of the first birds seen in spring.

13. The rabbit seemed to _____ as the magician waved his scarf.

14. We were allowed to _____ him at the hospital.

1 Replace the underlined words with a word from the box. Write the word on the line.

petals	widow	volume	tonic	tropics
relic	comet	novel	tribute	valid

1. Last night we saw a <u>star-like body with a tail of light</u> streak through the sky. _____

2. Thomas had a <u>factual, true</u> point to make about the new tax laws. _____

3. A rose has many <u>colored leaves</u>. _____

4. Cod-liver oil is a <u>drink that gives strength</u>; it contains vitamins A and D. _____

5. Andrew would like to take a cruise to the <u>hottest part of the earth around the equator</u>. _____

6. Memorial Day is a <u>way of showing respect and thanks</u> to our dead soldiers. _____

7. Helen Edison is a <u>woman whose husband is dead</u>. _____

8. Josh has a <u>new and unusual</u> plan for raising money for the clinic. _____

9. The <u>cubic space</u> of the fish tank is ten gallons. _____

10. This uniform is an <u>old object</u> from the Civil War. _____

Proofreading Practice

Two of the List 6 words are misspelled in each of the sentences. Cross out each misspelled word, and write the correct spelling above it.

1. Janet had nevver traveled by camel before her second visit to the dessert.

2. For our class project, we will studdy Halley's comet and make a modle of it.

3. Thomas is clevor to write both novvels and comic book scripts.

(1) **Read the sentences and circle all the List 6 words.**

1. Monica will order a large lemon wedge to go with the fresh melon.

2. Adam will donate a copy of that book to the prison.

3. Megan just read a clever novel about a magic dragon.

4. John never finds the time to polish his boots.

5. It was his habit to read comic books rather than to study his lessons.

6. Andrew put a radish in his fresh garden salad.

7. It must have been hard to travel across the desert in a covered wagon.

8. There are lots of rapids in the river by our cabin.

9. The comet streaked past the planet and then vanished from sight.

10. You can find a more modern product on the second level.

11. Josh hid Brendan's present in his bedroom closet.

(2) **Your teacher will dictate three of the sentences above. Write them on a blank piece of paper.**

(3) **Write a short story or a descriptive paragraph using ten words from List 6. Be creative!**

✔ Reading & Spelling Skill Check

Demonstrate your accuracy in reading and spelling List 6 words. Your teacher will select ten words to read and ten words to spell. Record your scores on the Accuracy Checklist. Work toward 90–100 percent accuracy.

Word Proficiency

Now build up your reading proficiency with List 6 words. Decide on your rate goal with your teacher. Record your progress on the Word Proficiency Graph.

My goal for reading List 6 is _____ words per minute with two or fewer errors.

(1) Practice the words, read the passage, and then answer the questions.

List 6 Words			Review Words	Passage Words	
metal	wagon	never	even	miner(s)	wildest
planet	rivers	magic	gathered	California	water
traveled	denim	method		shovels	fortune
				mother	

Gold in a Pan

Gold is the most prized metal on the planet, but it can be hard to find. In the Gold Rush of 1849, miners gathered in California to search for gold. They traveled by wagon or ship. Each miner dreamed of striking it rich.

The miners lined the rivers. They wore denim jeans and brought picks, shovels, and pans. Some struck the "mother load" and became rich beyond their wildest dreams. Some never found more than a few specks of the magic metal.

All a miner needed to find gold was a pan, time, and luck. The miners scooped up water and dirt from the river. They swirled the pan so the water and dirt spilled out. Sometimes, small specks or even big nuggets of gold were left behind.

It took a long time to build a fortune by this method, but the miners did not mind. To them, there was nothing more thrilling than the sight of gold in a pan.

1. What word from the text means "a way of doing something"? _____

2. Why did people go to California in 1849? _____

_____

3. What method for finding gold does the text tell about? _____

_____

(2) **FLUENCY** Decide on your fluency rate goal with your teacher. Record your progress on the Fluency Graph.

My goal for reading the passage is _____ words per minute with two or fewer errors.

able	cradle	kettle	puddle	stable
ankle	crinkle	little	purple	startle
apple	crumble	maple	puzzle	stifle
battle	cycle	marble	raffle	stumble
bottle	eagle	measles	rattle	table
bridle	fable	middle	riddle	temple
brittle	gentle	muscle	ruffle	thimble
bugle	gurgle	needle	saddle	tremble
bundle	handle	noble	sample	trifle
cable	hassle	paddle	settle	turtle
candle	huddle	pebble	simple	twinkle
castle	humble	people	single	uncle
cattle	hustle	pimple	sparkle	whistle
circle	idle	poodle	sprinkle	wrestle

Three-Syllable Words:

article   example   icicle   miracle   particle

The Consonant-*le* Syllable (C*le*)

A **C*le* syllable (C*le*)** is a final syllable. It has the schwa sound, so it sounds like consonant-/əl/.

Example: ple = /pəl/

Remember: A C*le* syllable is a final syllable. Don't confuse C*le* syllables with open syllables just because you see a vowel at the end.

(1) Circle all the C*le* syllables.

so	he	ple	pi
kle	hi	no	dle
we	ble	me	be
fle	zle	she	gle

(2) Write the C*le* syllables from Activity 1 on the lines. Then read them aloud, giving them the schwa sound.

_____

_____

_____

_____

_____

_____

_____

(3) Your teacher will dictate five consonant-*le* syllables. Repeat each syllable as you write it.

1. _____

2. _____

3. _____

4. _____

5. _____

The Double-Vowel Syllable (VV)

A **Double-Vowel Syllable (VV)** has two vowels that together make one sound. The sound has to be learned.

Examples: *oo* can say /o͞o/ as in *cool, ea* can say /ē/ as in *neat*

⑤ Review

An **open syllable (CV)** ends in one vowel. The vowel is usually long.

A **closed syllable (VC)** has one vowel, one consonant, and a short-vowel sound.

An **r-controlled syllable (Vr)** has a vowel followed by an *r*.

A **Cle syllable (Cle)** is a final syllable. The syllable sounds like consonant-/əl/.

① Write the syllables under the correct headings. Then read the syllables in each group.

ple	mar	fle	kle	poo	pur
cra	dle	trem	bot	i	mea
am	gle	cir	mus	ket	mir
gur	un	bi	ea	nee	tle

Consonant-*le* (C*le*)	Double-Vowel (VV)	Open (CV)	Closed (VC)	*r*-Controlled (V*r*)
_____	_____	_____	_____	_____
_____	_____	_____	_____	_____
_____	_____	_____	_____	_____
_____	_____		_____	_____
_____			_____	
			_____	

Consonant-*le* Syllabication Rule (*Cle*)

When a word ends in a consonant followed by *le,* you divide the syllables before the consonant. Count three letters from the end of the word and divide.

(1) Mark any long or short vowels in the first syllable. Say the syllables to read the whole word. Then draw a line to divide the syllables, and circle the consonant-*le* syllable.

stā	ble	s t a(b l e)	sam	ple	s a m p l e
pud	dle	p u d d l e	bu	gle	b u g l e
ea	gle	e a g l e	ruf	fle	r u f f l e
pur	ple	p u r p l e	bri	dle	b r i d l e
i	dle	i d l e	cir	cle	c i r c l e

(2) Match the syllables to make real words. Then say each word as you write it.

cy	ple	_____	pim	dle	_____
poo	tle	_____	cra	ple	_____
tem	cle	_____	gur	ble	_____
gen	dle	_____	stum	gle	_____
brit	ple	_____	twin	tle	_____
hud	ble	_____	bat	kle	_____
sta	dle	_____	bu	dle	_____
pur	tle	_____	nee	gle	_____

(3) Unscramble the syllables to make a real word.

am	ple	ex	_____
ti	ar	cle	_____
cle	a	mir	_____
i	cle	ci	_____

1 Your teacher will dictate twenty words. Spell the missing syllable. Then say the whole word as you write it.

1. _____ ple   _____

2. _____ gle   _____

3. _____ dle   _____

4. _____ dle   _____

5. _____ tle   _____

6. _____ ble   _____

7. _____ ble   _____

8. _____ dle   _____

9. _____ dle   _____

10. _____ dle   _____

11. fa _____   _____

12. peo _____   _____

13. puz _____   _____

14. bat _____   _____

15. ea _____   _____

16. mid _____   _____

17. gur _____   _____

18. cir _____   _____

19. ta _____   _____

20. ruf _____   _____

1. Add one of these consonant-*le* syllables to each syllable below. Then say the whole word as you write it.

ble	dle	tle	fle	kle

star_____ _____   han_____ _____

pad_____ _____   mar_____ _____

sta_____ _____   bot_____ _____

cat_____ _____   bat_____ _____

ca_____ _____   fa_____ _____

tur_____ _____   raf_____ _____

sad_____ _____   poo_____ _____

ta_____ _____   bun_____ _____

spar_____ _____   sprin_____ _____

twin_____ _____   cra_____ _____

2. Read the synonyms. Choose the correct word from Activity 1, and write it on the line.

bunch _____

scatter _____

twinkle _____

crib, bed _____

fight _____

rope, cord _____

surprise _____

story _____

Sometimes the consonant in a C*le* pattern is silent. For example, *tle* and *cle* are sometimes pronounced /əl/.

(1) **Fill in the missing *tle* or *cle* syllable. Then choose the correct word to complete the sentences.**

wres_____   **1.** The king and the queen live in a _____.

mus_____   **2.** To work rapidly is to _____.

whis_____   **3.** The tissue in our bodies that lets us move is called

_____.

cas_____   **4.** To fight with another person on a mat is to _____.

hus_____   **5.** The sound we can make with our mouth and lips is a

_____.

There are two ways to spell /kəl/: *cle* as in un<u>cle</u> and *kle* as in an<u>kle</u>.

(2) **Circle *kle* or *cle* in the following words. Then write them under the correct heading.**

crinkle   ankle   circle

sprinkle   sparkle   cycle

uncle   twinkle

kle   **cle**

_____   _____

_____   _____

_____   _____

_____

_____

(3) **QUICK CHECK Have another student test you on spelling these words.**

My score: _____ /_____ words correct

Review

When a word ends with a *Cle* syllable, divide the word into syllables before the *Cle*.
The accent is on the first syllable of most two-syllable words, including *Cle* words.

1 **Directions:**

- Draw a line to divide between the syllables.
- If the first vowel is long (‾) or short (ˇ), mark it.
- Draw a line though the *e* at the end of the word.
- Write the accented syllable in the box and the unaccented syllable on the line.

pĕb|blė̸ | peb | ___ble___   idle | ☐ | _____

huddle | ☐ | _____   noble | ☐ | _____

puddle | ☐ | _____   circle | ☐ | _____

bugle | ☐ | _____   riddle | ☐ | _____

stable | ☐ | _____   gurgle | ☐ | _____

poodle | ☐ | _____   cable | ☐ | _____

sample | ☐ | _____   stumble | ☐ | _____

uncle | ☐ | _____   tremble | ☐ | _____

purple | ☐ | _____   cattle | ☐ | _____

2 **Fill in the blank to describe the words in Activity 1.**

The final syllable is always a _____ syllable.

1 Draw lines to divide these words into syllables. Then write them under the correct headings.

cra|dle	circle	measles	sparkle
needle	purple	able	temple
cattle	poodle	marble	stable
humble	puddle	sample	idle

Closed		_Cle_
_____		_____
_____		_____
_____		_____
_____		_____
_____		_____

Open		_Cle_
cra		_dle_
_____		_____
_____		_____
_____		_____

_r_-Controlled		_Cle_
_____		_____
_____		_____
_____		_____
_____		_____

Double-Vowel		_Cle_
_____		_____
_____		_____
_____		_____

1 Your teacher will dictate sixteen words. If the first syllable has a long-vowel sound, write the word under the Open/C*le* column. If the first syllable has a short-vowel sound, write the word under the Closed/C*le* column, and be sure to double the middle consonant.

Closed / C*le* ăp/ple	Open/C*le* tā/ble
_____	_____
_____	_____
_____	_____
_____	_____
_____	_____
_____	_____
_____	_____
_____	

2 These words have silent letters. Practice spelling them.

people

pe ____ pl ____

_____

whistle

w ____ is ____ le

_____

muscle

mus ____ le

_____

1 Match the words in the box with the definitions below.

ankle	brittle	bugle	example	huddle
gurgle	article	stifle	idle	ruffle
humble	eagle	thimble	fable	miracle

Consonant-*le*

not working; lazy

a big bird; the U.S. symbol

between the foot and leg

a story with a lesson

a kind of horn used in the army

make a bubbling noise

to crowd together

to stop the breath of; smother

not proud

a strip of gathered cloth

used on the finger for sewing

easily broken

a wonderful happening; almost magic

a sample; a model

piece of writing in a newspaper or magazine

1 Fill in the blanks with words from the box.

purple	handle	apples	uncle	marbles	simple
ankle	circle	needle	turtle	middle	kettle
people	twinkle	single	able	sprinkle	eagle

1. Jamal sprained his _____ when he was picking

   _____ off the tree.

2. Do you want a _____ or double scoop of ice cream?

3. _____ the goblets with care.

4. My _____ will not be _____ to attend the

   family picnic. He is going to be out of town.

5. Grandma will sew your pants if you bring her the _____

   and thread.

6. Draw a big _____ in the _____ of

   your paper.

7. Many _____ like to look at the stars and watch them

   _____.

8. Robert wants to play a game of _____ with his friend.

9. A _____ is a reptile that has a hard outer shell.

10. It hasn't rained for a while. We should _____ the garden

    with water.

11. The color _____ is made by mixing red and blue.

12. Polly put the _____ on; we'll all have tea.

13. The bald _____ is a magnificent bird.

14. This arithmetic problem is quite _____.

Proofreading Practice

Two of the List 7 words are misspelled in each sentence. Rewrite the whole sentence, and spell the words correctly.

1. I wish that your poodle would settel down instead of running around in curcles.

_____

_____

2. The purple glass bottel sparkled on the marbble table.

_____

_____

3. Joel sprinkled pebbles in the puddle so the littel tertle could sit on them.

_____

_____

4. If you put a handdle on the middle bundle, you'll be abel to carry it.

_____

_____

5. It was a real hasell when Uncle Dave stumbled on the path and hurt his ancle.

_____

_____

6. The fabul about the turtle and the eegle teaches an important lesson.

_____

_____

7. It was a miracle that the cassle didn't crumble in the batle.

_____

_____

8. The baby gergled in her craydle, shook her rattle, and smiled.

_____

(1) Read the sentences and circle all the List 7 words.

1. I could not decide whether he had pimples or the measles.

2. Megan took the saddle and bridle back to the stable.

3. Martin was so little that he didn't have enough muscle to wrestle on the team.

4. The tailor got out his needle, thread, and thimble and sewed a ruffle on Jill's dress.

5. The eagle landed in the maple tree near a castle.

6. After the baby had her bottle, she gurgled a little, and then slept in the cradle.

7. My uncle would rather play marbles than do a puzzle.

8. Be gentle with the little poodle.

9. Lucy stumbled over the pebbles and sprained her ankle.

10. Most people like peanut butter.

11. Did you read the article about the thunderstorm? It is a miracle so many trees are still standing!

(2) Your teacher will dictate three of the sentences above. Write them on a blank piece of paper.

(3) Write a short story or descriptive paragraph using ten words from List 7. Be creative!

Reading & Spelling Skill Check

Demonstrate your accuracy in reading and spelling List 7 words. Your teacher will select ten words to read and ten words to spell. Record your scores on the Accuracy Checklist. Work toward 90–100 percent accuracy.

Word Proficiency

Now build up your reading proficiency with List 7 words. Decide on your rate goal with your teacher. Record your progress on the Word Proficiency Graph.

My goal for reading List 7 is _____ words per minute with two or fewer errors.

Practice Page | 7N

1 Practice the words, read the passage, and then answer the questions.

List 7 Words			Review Words		Passage Words	
sprinkle	little	gurgles	pancakes	cascades	syrup	enough
maple	middle	bottles	gallon(s)	travel	liquid	fifty
table	kettles	people	butter		nutrients	building
icicles	able					

Getting Maple Syrup to Your Table

Say that you are about to eat a huge stack of pancakes. Maybe you sprinkle on some fruit or put on some butter. Then you reach for the maple syrup. Do you ever think about how maple syrup gets to your table?

Maple syrup is made from sap, a liquid found in trees. The making of maple syrup starts in the spring, just as the snow and icicles start to melt. First, people who make the syrup drill a little hole in the middle of each maple tree. Then they stick a tube into the hole to get at the sap. The sap flows from many trees through many tubes to one big tank.

Next, the full tank is taken to a building. The sap goes into huge kettles to boil. You need about fifty gallons of sap to be able to make one gallon of syrup. Once the syrup is sweet enough, it gurgles into a new tank to cool. At last, the cool syrup cascades into bottles that travel in trucks to stores. In no time, that maple syrup is on your table.

1. What word from the text means "large pots"? _____

2. When does the making of maple syrup usually start? _____

_____

3. How many gallons of sap are needed to make one gallon of syrup? _____

_____

2 **FLUENCY** Record your progress on the Fluency Graph.

My goal for reading the passage is _____ words per minute with two or fewer errors.

/ā/	/ē/	/ī/	/ō/	/ū/ and /ōō/
chaos	Andrea	client	boa	continuum
chaotic	cameo	defiant	coerce	cruel
	create	dial	Joel	dual
	idea	Diana	Noel	duel
	ideal	diet	oasis	duet
	Leo	iodine	poem	duo
	meander	ion	poet	fluent
	meteor	iota		fluid
	museum	Iowa		fuel
	neon	lion		influence
	nucleus	pioneer		minuet
	react	quiet		ruin
	real	riot		truant
	really	science		
	rodeo	trial		
	Romeo	triumph		
		violence		
		violent		
		violet		
		violin		

Review

Double-Vowel Syllables (VV)

When a word or syllable has two vowels in a row, usually the vowels make one sound together. This is a Double-Vowel Syllable. These sounds must be learned.

① Circle the double vowels in these words. Then write the words under the correct headings. **Hint:** Sometimes *y* and *w* act as vowels.

flies	clay	fruit	blow
brief	doe	grew	sleigh
pay	team	break	goal
coast	moose	grow	lie
meal	seed	rain	group
blue	die	spies	tree

/ā/   **/ē/**   **/ō/**

_____ _____ _____

_____ _____ _____

_____ _____ _____

_____ _____ _____

_____ _____ _____

/ī/   **/ū/ or /o͞o/**

_____ _____ _____

_____ _____ _____

_____ _____ _____

_____

1 Circle the double vowels in these words. Then write them under the headings according to their vowel sounds.

crawl	mouse	shout	broil	town
oink	took	meant	taught	bread
haul	stood	joy	brook	health
sauce	round	boy		

/aw/ as in *saw*

_____

_____

_____

_____

/ow/ as in *cow*

_____

_____

_____

_____

/oi/ as in *oil*

_____

_____

_____

_____

/o͝o/ as in *look*

_____

_____

_____

/ĕ/ as in *head*

_____

_____

_____

⟳ Review

Double-Vowel syllables (VV) have _____ vowels that together make one sound.

The /aw/ sound can be spelled _____, _____, or _____.

The /ow/ sound can be spelled _____ or _____.

The /oi/ sound can be spelled _____ or _____.

The /o͝o/ sound is spelled _____.

The /ĕ/ sound is spelled _____.

① Label each syllable with the code below. Mark the long and short vowels, and read the syllables aloud to another student.

VC	**closed syllables**
VC*e*	**silent-*e* syllables**
CV	**open syllables**
V*r*	***r*-controlled syllables**

nē	_CV_	de	_____	umph	_____
id	_____	dine	_____	li	_____
tri	_____	sis	_____	mu	_____
et	_____	min	_____	cli	_____
cre	_____	der	_____	cam	_____
vi	_____	um	_____	o	_____
or	_____	fu	_____	os	_____

② Your teacher will dictate ten syllables. Repeat the syllables as you write them on the long lines.

1. _____ _____   6. _____ _____

2. _____ _____   7. _____ _____

3. _____ _____   8. _____ _____

4. _____ _____   9. _____ _____

5. _____ _____   10. _____ _____

③ Now use the code above to label these syllables.

⑤ Review

Double-Vowel syllables or words (VV) have two vowels that together make one sound.

① Read these double-vowel words aloud.

true	foam
suit	mean
toe	ties

V/V Syllabication Rule

If two vowels together do not make a recognizable word when sounded as a double vowel, divide between the vowels. This gives the first of the two vowels its long sound.

② Read the words aloud.

VV Words	die	boat	due	read
V/V Words	di|et	bo|a	du|et	re|act

③ These words follow the V/V Rule. Draw a line to separate the syllables, and mark the first vowel long (⁻). Then read the words aloud.

n e o n	f u e l	c h a o s
d u e l	l i o n	f l u i d
c l i e n t	d i e t	p o e m
r u i n	r i o t	t r i u m p h

1. Mark the first vowel in the V/V combination long (ˉ). Say each syllable to read the whole word. Then draw a line to divide the syllables as shown.

trī	al	tri	al	tri	umph		t r i u m p h
re	act	r e a c t	co	erce		c o e r c e
cre	ate	c r e a t e	sci	ence		s c i e n c e
ru	in	r u i n	i	de	a	i d e a
cha	os	c h a o s	I	o	wa	I o w a
po	et	p o e t	in	flu	ence	i n f l u e n c e
qui	et	q u i e t	mu	se	um	m u s e u m

2. Circle the two vowels in each word that follow the V/V Syllabication Rule. Mark the first vowel sound in the V/V combination long (ˉ). Then write the words on the lines.

n u c l e u s   _____

r o d e o   _____

v i o l i n   _____

p i o n e e r   _____

i o d i n e   _____

o a s i s   _____

m i n u e t   _____

m e a n d e r   _____

i n f l u e n c e   _____

v i o l e n c e   _____

When the last syllable of a word is the schwa sound, it is spelled with the letter *a*.

Example: Diana

1 Fill in the missing *a,* and write the whole word. Then write a sentence using two of the words.

ide_____   _____   iot_____   _____

low_____   _____   bo_____   _____

_____

_____

The pattern *et* is a common way to spell /ət/ or /ĭt/ at the end of words.

2 Fill in the missing syllable *et,* and write the whole word.

po _____   _____   qui _____   _____

vi o l _____   _____   di _____   _____

The patterns *ent* and *ant* are common ways to spell /ənt/ at the end of words.

3 Fill in the missing syllable, and write the whole word.

| **Add *ent*** | **Add *ant*** |

cli _____   _____   tru _____   _____

flu _____   _____   de fi _____   _____

vi o l _____   _____

4 **QUICK CHECK** Have another student test you on spelling these words.

My score: _____ /_____ words correct

(1) Your teacher will dictate twelve words. Spell the missing syllable. Then say the whole word as you write it.

1. _____ on _____

2. _____ id _____

3. po _____ _____

4. _____ o lin _____

5. cre _____ _____

6. i _____ a _____

7. l o _____ _____

8. _____ se _____ _____

9. ro _____ o _____

10. i o _____ _____

11. _____ et _____

12. in _____ ence _____

(2) Now choose three words and use them in sentences.

_____

_____

_____

_____

_____

_____

The **V/V Syllabication Rule** is the last and least common syllabication rule. Only a few words divide between the vowels. The first vowel in the V/V combination is always long since the syllable is open. In most cases, the accent is on the first syllable.

1 Divide between the vowels and mark the first vowel of the V/V combination long (⁻). Write the word by syllables and note the accent pattern.

n ē | o n | n̄e | _o n_

t r u a n t | | _____

d u e t   _____ | |

p o e t | | _____

c r e a t e   _____ | |

d i e t | | _____

m e t e o r | | _____ _____

o a s i s   _____ | | _____

v i o l i n   _____ _____ | |

m u s e u m   _____ | | _____

n u c l e u s | | _____ _____

i n f l u e n c e | | _____ _____

1 Some of the words listed here are one-syllable words that contain a double vowel (VV). Other words are two-syllable words that divide between the vowels (V/V). Decide if the words are one-syllable or two-syllable words. Then write them under the correct heading.

suit	lion	science	boa
quiet	spoil	pie	poach
trial	react	toe	dial
paint	preach	poet	jail
truant	ruin	fruit	duet

One-Syllable Words (VV)

_____

_____

_____

_____

_____

_____

_____

_____

Two-Syllable Words (V/V)

_____

_____

_____

_____

_____

_____

_____

_____

_____

Proofreading Practice

Two of the List 8 words are misspelled in each of the sentences. Rewrite the whole sentence, and spell the words correctly.

1. It seemed crule of the lyon to kill the ostrich.

_____

_____

2. My client's triel began in a quite courtroom and ended in a chaotic one.

_____

_____

3. Diana had a novel ideah for a sience fair project.

_____

_____

4. The pome was about a dule between Romeo and his rival.

_____

_____

5. The pote wrote about poneers who struggled and triumphed.

_____

_____

6. The road to the museme twists and turns and meyanders along the river.

_____

_____

7. Snakes like the boah eat a dite of rats, birds, and bats.

_____

_____

8. My drawing was runed when some fluade dripped on it and stained it.

_____

_____

Practice Page **8K**

/əl/ at the end of some common V/V words is spelled *al* or *el*.

(1) Circle the last two letters in each of these words. Then write the words under the correct heading.

trial   duel   ideal   real

cruel   dial   dual   fuel

           al   *el*

_____   _____

_____   _____

_____   _____

_____

_____

(2) Complete the puzzle with the words from Activity 1.

Across
2. perfect
5. trying a case in court
7. not fake

Down
1. to call on a phone
3. a fight between two people to settle a quarrel
4. mean; causing pain
6. a material that is burned to make heat or power

/ən/ in these words is spelled *on*.

(3) Fill in the missing syllable, and then write the whole word.

li ____ ____ _____   pi ____ ____ eer _____

1 Read the definitions. Choose the correct word from the box, and write it on the line.

neon	truant	triumph	nucleus
cameo	fluent	defiant	iota

easy flowing; good in language   _____

very small amount   _____

openly resisting   _____

a gas used in signs   _____

a student who skips school   _____

the central part of an atom   _____

oval-shaped jewelry with carved image   _____

victory; success   _____

2 Fill in the blanks with words from the box.

really	dial	idea
quiet	lion	diet
trial	duel	cruel

1. A good _____ includes lots of fruits and vegetables.

2. Mr. Leopold is on _____ for murder.

3. The _____ on the car radio doesn't work.

4. The _____ in the cage roared; it was not a

   _____ sound.

5. Do you have any _____ what time it is? I have a feeling it's

   _____ late.

6. The two _____ men fought a _____.

(1) Read the sentences and circle all the List 8 words.

1. The idea inspired the poet to create a poem.

2. Which animal would you fear more, a lion or a boa constrictor?

3. The defiant pioneer braved the cruel Iowa winter.

4. There is a new model of a nucleus at the science museum.

5. The violin duet was followed by a lively minuet.

6. Staying on his diet was a major triumph for Leo.

7. The neon light made everything look violet.

8. A quiet student like Andrea is good to have in a chaotic classroom.

9. When the car ran out of fuel on the highway, Julia reacted badly.

10. Salt can provide the iodine needed in our diet.

11. Diana likes to meander through the garden oasis in the middle of the city.

(2) Your teacher will dictate three of the sentences. Write them on a blank piece of paper.

(3) Write a short story or a descriptive paragraph using ten words from List 8. Be creative!

Reading & Spelling Skill Check

Demonstrate your accuracy in reading and spelling List 8 words. Your teacher will select ten words to read and ten words to spell. Record your scores on the Accuracy Checklist. Work toward 90–100 percent accuracy.

Word Proficiency

Now build up your reading proficiency with List 8 words. Decide on your rate goal with your teacher. Record your progress on the Word Proficiency Graph.

My goal for reading List 8 is _____ words per minute with two or fewer errors.

1 Practice the words, read the passage, and then answer the questions.

List 8 Words			Review Words	Passage Words	
poem(s)	rodeo	ideas	people	poetry	festivals
poets	pioneer	ideal	cattle	serious	celebrate
real	quiet		modern	country	music
create	influence		hundreds		

Cowboy Poetry

We call them cowpokes, rodeo riders, or cowboys. They are the strong people who ride the range and herd the cattle. Some of them are poets, too.

Cowboy poetry started in the pioneer days of the Old West. Cowboys had to create their own fun. They told tales, sang songs, and made up poems. Some wrote down their poems, and soon people started to read about life on the range.

There is no ideal cowboy poem. They can be about the Old West, or they can have more modern themes. Most are about cowboy life. Many are fun, but there are sad, serious cowboy poems, too. The ideas in cowboy poetry are a lot like those in country music. The two art forms influence each other.

Cowboy poetry now has many fans. There are hundreds of cowboy poets and books of poetry. Each year many festivals celebrate this art form. In fact, one week in April is named Cowboy Poetry Week.

1. What word from the text means "make"? _____

2. How did cowboy poetry start? _____

   _____

3. How are cowboy poetry and country music alike? _____

   _____

2 **FLUENCY** Record your progress on the Fluency Graph.

My goal for reading the passage is _____ words per minute with two or fewer errors.

absorb	daytime	item	partner	sailboat
anything	dictate	kettle	persist	salad
athlete	drugstore	kitten	poet	sherbet
bacon	eagle	legal	pretzel	silver
basic	escort	lemon	prison	snowball
basket	everyone	limit	problem	sober
bugle	explode	lion	publish	study
camel	further	lobster	punish	subject
carbon	handle	locate	puppet	sunshine
chaos	happen	mental	purple	suppose
collide	humid	menu	puzzle	surplus
complete	hustle	model	quiet	temple
copy	idea	necktie	ribbon	tiny
costume	insane	noble	rival	tonsil
crater	intrude	oasis	rodeo	twinkle
cruel	invade	oatmeal	rubber	unit
curtsy	Iowa	outlaw	ruin	without

(1) Draw a line to divide the words into syllables.

l e m o n	q u i e t	h a n d l e	c h a o s
h u m i d	c r a t e r	p u z z l e	c a m e l
t w i n k l e	l e g a l	r u i n	m o d e l

(2) Now sort these words according to the syllabication rule you used.

V/CV	VC/V	/Cle	V/V
_____	_____	_____	_____
_____	_____	_____	_____
_____	_____	_____	_____

(3) Match the syllables to make a real word. Then say the word as you write it.

out	ject	_outlaw_____
with	law	_____
sub	zel	_____
pret	out	_____
in	bet	_____
cos	vade	_____
sher	cort	_____
es	tume	_____

④ **Read the definitions. Choose the correct word in the box, and write it on the lines. Then use the numbered letters to answer the question below.**

menu	hustle	daytime	purple
happen	bacon	sailboat	

a boat with a sail

— — — — — — — —
1   2

a meat, often served with eggs

— — — —
3   4

the color made by mixing red and blue

— — — — — —
5

the part of a day that has natural light

— — — — — — —
6

a list of foods you can order at a restaurant

— — — —
7

to work quickly

— — — — — —
8

to take place

— — — — — —
9

What kind of syllable ends in one vowel? — — — — — — — — — — — —
2 5 7 4   1 6 8 8 9 3 8 7

 Proofreading Practice

Two of the Review List words are misspelled in each sentence. Cross out each misspelled word, and write the correct spelling above it.

1. Please don't say enything mean about my latest wild idia!

2. I could solve the math problom if the room was quiat.

3. Vincent likes the special lemin dressing his mother makes for saleds.

4. Sofia's studey partener helped her pass the test.

5. I can't compleet my project withowt more information.

(5) **Draw a line to match the words to the definitions.**

athlete	an extra amount
basket	a ball made of snow
bugle	someone who is good at sports
snowball	mean; causing pain
surplus	having to do with the law
prison	a straw container
legal	a place where people stay as punishment for a crime
cruel	something that makes music; like a trumpet

(6) **Circle the words in the word search below. The words can be found across or down.**

suppose	unit	collide	absorb	basic	noble	tiny
subject	insane	rodeo	salad	sunshine	intrude	copy
anything	explode	everyone	eagle	oasis	limit	

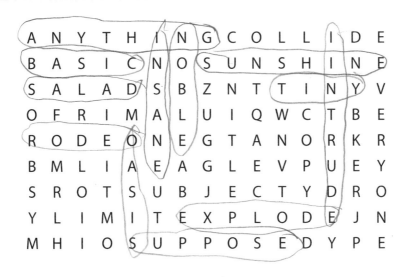

Syllable Types and Syllabication Rules

The Six Types of Syllables

Closed (VC)
A closed syllable has only one vowel and ends in a consonant. The vowel is usually short: *ad, sug, lish, trom, ject.*

Silent-*e* (VCe)
A silent-*e* syllable has one vowel followed by a consonant followed by an *e*. The *e* is silent and makes the preceding vowel long: *plete, mune, stroke, ope, mate.*

Open (CV)
An open syllable ends in one vowel. The vowel is usually long: *pi, glo, stri, u, cy, re.*

***r*-Controlled (V*r*)**
An *r*-controlled syllable has a vowel followed by an *r*, which modifies the vowel sound: *car, mer, fir, cor, tur.*

Consonant-*le* (C*le*)
A consonant-*le* syllable is a final syllable in which the *e* is silent; thus it sounds like consonant-əl: *ta-ble, jun-gle, sim-ple, bu-gle.*

Double-Vowel (VV)
A double-vowel syllable has two vowels that together make one sound. This sound has to be learned, as it often takes on a sound different from either single vowel: *boat, fie, haul, voy, floun.*

The Five Syllabication Rules

VC/CV
When two or more consonants stand between two vowels, divide between the consonants, so that consonant blends and digraphs stay together: *pup-pet, hun-dred, sup-pose, fan-tas-tic.*

V/CV
When a single consonant is surrounded by two vowels, you usually divide the word into syllables before the consonant, making the vowel in the first syllable long: *hu-man, lo-cate, pi-lot, e-ven.*

VC/V
If the V/CV Syllabication Rule doesn't make a real word, divide the syllables after the consonant, and give the vowel its short sound: *rap-id, sol-id, cab-in, stud-y.*

/C*le*
Divide the syllables before the consonant-*le*. Count three letters from the end of the word and divide: *star-tle, sta-ble, ea-gle.*

V/V
Divide only a few words between the vowels. The vowel in the first syllable is always long: *di-et, flu-id, qui-et, i-o-dine.*

Accuracy Checklist

Megawords 1, Lists 1–8

Name _____ Carla _____

Word List	Examples	Check Test Scores Date:		Reading Skill Check			Spelling Skill Check		
		Reading	Spelling						
1. Compound Words	without haystack	8/10	9/10						
2. VC/CV Closed Syllables	tonsil splendid								
3. VC/CV Closed and Silent-*e* Syllables	stampede escape								
4. VC/CV Closed and *r*-Controlled Syllables	lobster garlic								
Review List: 1–4									
5. V/CV	tulip raven								
6. VC/V	relish comet								
7. /C*le*	stumble purple								
8. V/V	diet fluid								
Review List: 1–8									

Record accuracy score as a fraction: # correct
                                        # attempted

Word Proficiency Graph

Name _____

Goal _____

●———● Words read correctly in one minute (WCPM)

✕———✕ Errors

WCPM

80

70

60

50

40

30

20

10

Errors

0

Word List* _____

Date _____

Errors _____

WCPM** _____

* Repeat Word Lists as many times as needed.

**Word Count Per Minute (WCPM) = Words read in one minute - Errors

Word Proficiency Graph

Name _____

Goal _____

●———● Words read correctly in one minute (WCPM)

✗———✗ Errors

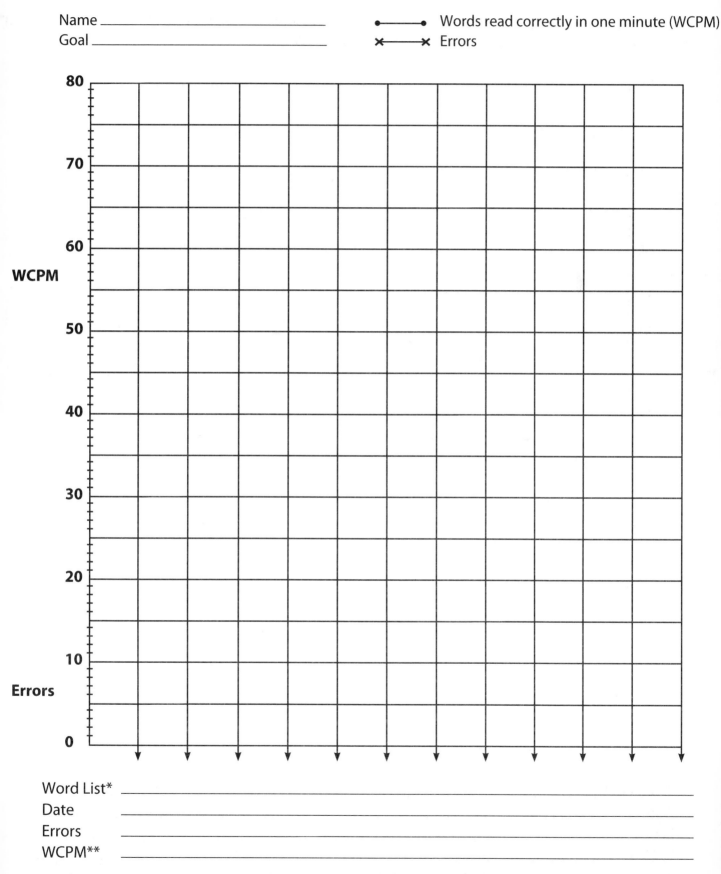

WCPM

80

70

60

50

40

30

20

10

Errors

5

0

Word List* _____

Date _____

Errors _____

WCPM** _____

* Repeat Word Lists as many times as needed.　　**Word Count Per Minute (WCPM) = Words read in one minute - Errors

Fluency Graph

Name _____

Goal _____

●————● Words read correctly in one minute (WCPM)

✗————✗ Errors

WCPM

160

140

120

100

80

60

40

20

Errors

0

Passage*   1

Date   4/20/10

Errors   2

WCPM**   134

* Repeat Passages as many times as needed.   **Word Count Per Minute (WCPM) = Words read in one minute - Errors

EXAMINER'S RECORDING FORM — READING

Check Test: Lists 1–8

Megawords 1

Name _____ Date _____

1. Compound Words

handball
sailboat
anywhere
barefoot
playmate

correct _____

2. VC/CV Closed Syllables

splendid
basket
coffin
establish
fantastic

correct _____

3. VC/CV Closed and Silent-e Syllables

trombone
commune
reptile
indispose
confiscate

correct _____

4. VC/CV Closed and r-Controlled Syllables

hermit
morbid
urban
permanent
carpenter

correct _____

5. V/CV

virus
veto
cupid
pilot
basin

correct _____

6. VC/V

rapid
denim
topic
punish
comic

correct _____

7. /Cle

cable
tremble
hustle
startle
ankle

correct _____

8. V/V

boa
fluid
diet
meander
iodine

correct _____

Total Correct _____

Total Possible _40_

EXAMINER'S RECORDING FORM — READING

Name _____   Date _____

1. Compound Words

handball

sailboat

anywhere

barefoot

playmate

correct _____

2. VC/CV Closed Syllables

splendid

basket

coffin

reptile

establish

fantastic

correct _____

3. VC/CV Closed and Silent-e Syllables

trombone

commune

reptile

indispose

confiscate

correct _____

4. VC/CV Closed and r-Controlled Syllables

hermit

morbid

urban

permanent

carpenter

correct _____

5. V/CV

virus

veto

cupid

pilot

basin

correct _____

6. VC/CV

rapid

denim

topic

punish

comic

correct _____

7. /Cle

cable

tremble

hustle

startle

ankle

correct _____

8. V/V

boa

fluid

diet

meander

iodine

correct _____

Total Correct _____

Total Possible _40_